PRIEST IN THE PRESBYTERY

PRIEST IN THE PRESBYTERY

A Psycho-Ecclesiastical Extravaganza

by

BERNARD BASSET, S.J.

With illustrations by
PENELOPE HARTER

HERDER AND HERDER

1966
HERDER AND HERDER NEW YORK
232 Madison Avenue, New York 10016

DE LICENTIA SUPERIORUM ORDINIS

NIHIL OBSTAT: JOANNES M. T. BARTON, S.T.D., L.S.S.
CENSOR DEPUTATUS
IMPRIMATUR: PATRITIUS CASEY
VICARIUS GENERALIS
WESTMONASTERII: DIE IIA JUNII 1964

Library of Congress Catalog Card Number: 65–29206
Printed in the United States of America

TO PAT

WHO HAS HELPED ME SO OFTEN
IN SO MANY UNUSUAL WAYS

CONTENTS

FOREWORD

No SERIOUS PURPOSE prompted the writing of this trivial book. *Priest in the Presbytery* draws no moral, passes no message, reports no objective incidents. If asked, the author would describe his book quite simply as a psycho-ecclesiastical extravaganza, and leave it at that.

Plumhampton, having no existence, cannot be assigned to any diocese. From this follows a logical deduction that the author was never its parish priest. He dissociates himself entirely from all the views herein expressed. The characters are all fictitious, with no intentional likeness to living parishioners. If the names of a few famous authors and journals have been included, this was done with deep affection and with the tongue in the cheek.

A book may be fictional and yet truthful, and it rests with each reader to determine how far Plumhampton is true to type. The author would be sad indeed if his quips and irrelevances should cause any personal offence. He is hoping, not against hope, that a certain disguised affection is discernible, together with a great pride in a vocation which made him very happy at eighteen and makes him hilarious at fifty-five. Naturally enough, his own order suffers some "digs" in the course of the story, thus providing an excuse for saying at the very beginning how very charming all his fellow Jesuits are.

9

Most of this book appeared in the form of articles in the *Catholic Herald*, in truncated form. The author is grateful to the *Catholic Herald* for permission to re-publish and for so many other kindnesses over so many years. Miss Harter kindly agreed to provide the illustrations though, under another name, she has a growing family with which to cope. Without her consent, the story of Plumhampton would never have been told.

The author received many letters during the serialization of his story, the majority happy, three bitter, two shocked. The most gratifying came from the Mother Prioress of a Carmelite convent, delighted that her community had had a good laugh. She informed the author that St Teresa of Avila promised a special blessing on those who thus amused the sisters; he remains very content if he qualifies for that.

B. B.

Bournemouth
15th April 1964

Chapter One

APPOINTMENT TO PLUMHAMPTON

I WOULD HAVE LIKED to pretend that I was on my knees with the Psalter open before me, when the bishop's letter arrived. Only saints, from long practice, time their devotion perfectly. In fact, I was just back from Mass at the convent and was resting on my bed with my shoes on. One eye, if I remember right, was gauging the distance to the nearest ashtray, the other was firmly fixed on the far end of my cigarette. I slit the envelope carelessly.

Great events happen so quickly; I was already parish priest of St Gertrude's, Plumhampton, when I sprang from the bed to blow the ash from the sheets. I suppose that I should have guessed that my turn for promotion was fast approaching but, after twenty years as a curate, promotion seems no more real than death. Besides, to the curates of a diocese, all parish priests look disappointingly fit.

His Lordship's letter was full of the bonhomie of the Vatican Council, all Christian names and encouragement. He thought that I would do great work for God in Plumhampton and, in those first moments of careless rapture, I was silly enough to feel the same myself. Plumhampton itself meant little to me. It sounded English enough and rural enough to suggest thatched cottages grouped artistically round a Maypole but, in our diocese at any rate, priests are very, very afraid of old English names. Take the sad case of poor Father Joe Plaster, appointed to St Hyacinth's, Mulberry-under-Trill. He, too, had his visions but these did not include the canal at the back of his presbytery. He cannot see the Power Station from his bedroom window for there is a gasometer in between. No, the faith normally flourishes in ugly places and I duly noted the thought in the back of my breviary, for a new parish priest cannot afford to squander his first bright ideas. After that, I gazed in the mirror and tried to deduce what Plumhampton was likely to think.

I had often motored through Plumhampton but without experiencing any great urge to stop. It looked the kind of district from which people come, but to which few in their senses go. One had heard diocesan organizers say, "I suppose we may count on a coach load from Plumhampton," but no one had ever suggested in my presence, "Let's take the altar boys to Plumhampton for the day." Still, on this day of days, Plumhampton sounded thrilling and I was moved enough to kneel for a moment in sincere but distracted prayer.

I was to hear a good deal about Plumhampton, not all of it accurate or flattering, in those last sad days before I sped away. I had to break the news of my promotion carefully. If my former fellow curates mourned to see me go, they did not show it; in our diocese we never display our feelings and leave the gentler emotions to the Regulars. Further, one must accept that there is bound to be a subtle change of feeling between curates still serving their sentence and one whose time is up. Slowly, but inevitably, the gap between us would widen; at the moment of appointment, a new parish priest is a sitting duck.

We had Plumhampton sixty times a day. My former fellow curates offered me bright ideas for liturgical reform, suggestions for ecumenical dialogue and many tips for dealing with the Reverend Mother, who, they said, held the British All-comers record, having broken

one canon and sixteen curates since her simple pro-
fession, fifty years before.

To listen to the curates, Plumhampton seemed a
straightforward cross between Belsen and Colney
Hatch. The weeds, they said, completely obscured the
presbytery windows; the former incumbent liked them
that way for they recalled his happy boyhood on the
Shannon and he would sit for hours, gun in hand, by
the dining-room window, waiting for the duck to rise.

I smiled benignly, practising by easy stages that
paternal expression of tolerance and resignation which
proves so useful in pastoral life. I had not perfected it
yet and the curates continued unabashed. I gathered
that I would have among my parishioners two famous
anonymous letter-writers known to the vicar general
and to the police. There had been many burglaries at
Plumhampton last year, in one of which all the relics
from the sacristy were swiped. Masked men with holy

water in their pistols had called to demand the authentification papers on the following day.

My paternal smile was improving and I nodded approvingly, as the Curé of Ars might have done had he had to deal with such heavy British humour; my former fellow curates must be allowed their moment of amusement; it would be years before they had to shoulder the heavy burden of a parish priest!

In fact, I found the burden surprisingly light, but Joe Plaster came over from Mulberry-under-Trill especially to warn me not to disclose this fact to anyone. Said Joe, "You should say to yourself, sixteen times a day on rising, 'A parish priest is run to death.' Unless you really believe this yourself, you can hardly expect to persuade the parishioners to sympathize."

At night in my room I read many improving books. My fellow curates brought me copies of Manning, Knox, Heenan and Ripley, who all have written helpful advice for priests. I learned that a parish priest must be humble, learned, firm, prayerful, tolerant and saintly, but, most of all, he must try to be himself.

My face in the mirror looked extraordinarily unconvincing but I hastily banished the fleeting thought that a purple stock might, somehow, help it; instead I fell on my knees to beg God to help me find my feet.

No tears were shed in the presbytery in the days following my appointment but I came near to tears when saying good-bye to old friends. Poor old Mrs Hurn was not fooled when I told her that she was looking better and that she would be over to see me at Plumhampton within a couple of months. "Why are you going, Father?" she kept on repeating. "I always hoped

that you would be here to give me confidence at the
end." How much of a priest's time is spent in imparting
to others a confidence which he does not feel himself!

There was a faint note of anticlimax in the days following my appointment as parish priest. If I, who should
have known better, felt a twinge of disappointment,
you, too, may be surprised by the absence of panache.
Why, Rome is famous for its ceremonial. We, who are
now familiar with pontifical functions on TV and the
measured movement of massed monsignori, would have
expected at least a small whiff of incense for a new
parish priest. For me, on my humble appointment to
St Gertrude's, Plumhampton, there was no more than the
bishop's kindly letter and the curates' less kindly jokes.
One had always vaguely hoped that one would be let
into some mighty secret, first whispered to Timothy or
Titus by the great St Paul. A miniature papal bull would
have done or a parchment covered with seals and
squiggles such as the faithful buy for a few lire in the
shops of Rome. I needed something to show my ageing
mother, who was slightly sceptical about my promotion, having failed to find Plumhampton on any map.
I received one impressive testimonial but this I dared
not show her, a scurrilous charter composed by one of
my fellow curates and designed by one of the sisters,
art mistress at the school. There was, also, a letter from
a famous firm of altar wine importers, congratulating
me and the diocese on my appointment and calling my
august attention to the bishop of Evora, who refused all
altar wine other than their own.
Joe Plaster, it was, who reassured me, promising me

a parchment, keys and a whiff of incense at my induction several months ahead. "You'll need it more then," he remarked in his casual way, "for by that time you should know more of the state of the roof and of the debt on the schools." Joe also warned me of the spiritual reaction which most new parish priests experience. "Exaltation", said he, "normally sets in two hours after appointment and may last in extreme cases for as long as four days. Next, there supervenes a phase of partial coma, after which one is usually 'fed up' for a period ranging from eight to ten years." In just such a state of coma, I packed my clothes, survived the shock of re-reading some of my earlier sermons, decided that Plumhampton had done nothing to deserve them, so destroyed them for good. My former fellow curates thought this an unkindly act, pictured my future biographer wasting hours in the diocesan archives, seeking to discover what the holy man had done with his time in his curate years.

Our farewells when they came were swift and poignant in the approved, diocesan, stiff-upper-lip style.

"Ee, so you're off at last, lad," said my former parish priest, and this, I assure you, was deeply moving, for in ten years of apostolic work together I had never before known him to use seven words where four would do.

"We'll be seeing you," cried the curates as I drove away but I, who was now determined to be humble, learned, firm, prayerful, tolerant and saintly, made certain mental reservations about this.

The housekeeper, too, maintained the glorious diocesan tradition. "We'll miss you, Father," she said almost tearfully, "but not, I hope, anything else from your room."

The nuns also sent a farewell note, beautifully inscribed on parchment; I read it at Plumhampton and was duly impressed. It read: "Wait on quietly in this land of yours; all shall be building now, not destroying, all shall be planting now, not uprooting; amends enough is the calamity that I have brought on you" (Jeremias 42.10).

In warmer and more dramatic climes, they can afford to let go a little; one has seen photographs of the present Holy Father on his knees and kissing the soil of Milan when taking possession of his See. The thought flitted through my mind, but Manning, Knox, Heenan and Ripley say nothing in favour of the practice, while the soil of Plumhampton is perhaps less inviting than the soil of Milan. Further, the housekeeper was waiting on the step to greet me and I did not want her to say to herself, "So he's one of those!"

Our meeting was therefore much more simple:

"I've come," said I.

"So you've come," said she.

"Let's come in," we exclaimed together, and the nearest that I came to kissing the soil of Plumhampton was the whispered ejaculation, "Come, Holy Ghost, Creator, come."

Of course I was very cautious and very careful during my first days at Plumhampton, especially on the first night. Joe Plaster had placed much importance on first impressions. "Watch your image, old man, for the first couple of years!" I wore my best soutane to show that I was clean and tidy, with two buttons undone to give the right impression of broadmindedness. I also had

my slogan handy, "We'll wait and see, shall we?" This
last did not produce the right effect on the first evening.
When the housekeeper asked if I would like my tea in
the dining-room, study or kitchen, my "We'll wait and
see, shall we?" was taken to mean that I did not want
tea at all. Still, I was both happy and excited and Pope
Leo XIII, in a broken frame, tucked away behind a sofa
in the parlour, looked affectionately at me as though he
was now expecting better days.

Joe Plaster had advised me, "Make no judgment for
the first eight years and then jump to no hasty conclusions," so I need not commit to paper the rash
decisions of my first evening as a parish priest. Perhaps
I felt just a little bit depressed. One cannot sit indefin-
itely in a half-furnished room, reading Manning, Knox,
Heenan or Ripley, and I filled up the evening wandering
round the house. So it came about that I discovered an
old and most stimulating pamphlet under the mattress
in the spare room.

It was entitled *Gleanings from Saint Gertrude* (London, 1890) and there was one passage marked with
purple ink. How encouraging it was to think that some
previous venerable parish priest had read the gleanings
of our common patron and was stayed up as I was by her
words. I read the pamphlet in my bed. Said St Gertrude:
"Remember, Sisters, that today's thorns will blossom
into tomorrow's nosegay," and if the phone had not
rung at that very moment, I might well have fallen
asleep with that lovely thought.

It was my former fellow curates, wanting to know if
all was well with the new parish priest. In a fatherly
tone I assured them that everything was.

"How are you getting on with St Gertrude?" they enquired flippantly, and then added, "We marked the best passage in purple; it has been our common experience, though we cannot explain it, that a new parish priest invariably snoops about the house disapprovingly and looks under the mattress in the spare room."

Chapter Two

EARLY DAYS

1. THE WIND OF CHANGE

I MYSELF am deeply puzzled for, though we invite the Holy Spirit of God to renew the face of the earth, we expect him to do so without altering the world or our arrangements in any way. In Plumhampton, at least, change is the one sin (see Luke 12) which can never be forgiven until the priest who dared to change things is himself changed. When he has paid the price, settled into the rut or been discreetly removed to serve as chaplain in some remote region, then he becomes the embodiment of sound tradition, to be quoted to his successor, day after day. One is told, "Father always kept the matches on the second shelf; Father washed the purificators on Wednesday, not on Tuesday; Father did not remove his goloshes until after he had put the Holy Oils away." St Gertrude was probably right when she saw today's thorns changing into tomorrow's nosegay but, had she known Plumhampton, she would never have risked the fatal word "change". Joe Plaster blanched on the phone when I told him on my first morning that I had changed the position of the bell on

21

the sacristy shelf. "Gosh, man," said he, and he only speaks like this when he is very frightened, "do go very, very slowly; when I came to this place, I scarcely dared to change my shirt for a couple of months."

It was silly about the bell because I had firmly resolved to change absolutely nothing and only moved it because I chanced to hit it with my elbow while searching for the *Ritual*. As I could not recall its exact position, I replaced it in the most convenient place.

Within sixteen minutes, two very devoted sacristy

workers had sensed the wind of change. "I see you've changed the bell, Father," remarked Miss Anstey sweetly, obviously accepting the alteration as just another little cross. "Ah well," added Mrs Gregory, sighing, "I'm sure Father has his very good reasons; most priests have their own funny little ways."

When I ordered the *Guardian* at the paper shop, Mrs Murphy, after welcoming me cordially in Plumhampton Irish, resumed the same theme. "So you'll be changing your paper, will you now?" she remarked with a slight emphasis on changing; "I hear there are to be great changes up at the presbytery." From the tone of her voice and the look in her eye one might have suspected that I was secretly planning a change of faith. I made a mental note that it might be necessary to alert the Plumhampton Fire Brigade if and when there was question of liturgical reform.

My former fellow curates were on the phone at lunchtime, not yet taking our new relationship seriously. "Gee, man," they said, "we never knew that you had it in you to change things so vigorously. Mrs Murphy on the phone tells us that you are another Oliver Cromwell, that you'll have Plumhampton on or off the map in a couple of weeks."

"But I've only moved a bell," said I, defensively.

"Don't excuse yourself," said they, "take a bold line and we'll support you with the vicar general—but fancy you changing the 'Hail, Holy Queen' on the very first morning, putting Plumhampton in 'this vale', rather than 'valley of tears'!"

I changed no more after that. "We'll wait and see, shall we?" turned from a slogan into an article of faith. A parish priest must be humble, learned, firm, tolerant, prayerful, saintly, but none of my approved authors made any reference to change. I was up at the school, round to the hospital, out with the lawn-mower, down

with the boiler; today's thorns remained thorns and tomorrow's nosegay would have to wait.

And then one morning, a week later, I could not find
my spectacle case. I knew that I had left it, as I always
did, on the shelf in the sacristy by the vesting table but
it had gone when I came off the altar after Mass. I
asked the housekeeper, who told Miss Anstey, who
consulted Mrs Gregory and Mrs Murphy, who sent out
an S.O.S. to the headmaster at the school. One of the
altar boys might have shifted it. Mrs Begorrah was just
cranking up for a novena to St Anthony to find it when
Miss Anstey remembered that she had changed it to a
safer place.

It was brought to me in my sitting-room in solemn
procession and I decided without thinking to deliver
my first pastoral homily. The powers of a parish priest
look truly impressive even in the Canon Law books, but
more is added when they are conveyed by word of
mouth. The whole magisterium of the Church was behind me for my opening sentence, "You simply must
not start changing things about without my permission,"
but then, unaccountably, I started to laugh.

The sacristy helpers certainly looked a little astonished, they could not guess that the one famous word
had stuck in my throat. "You must not start changing
things without my permission"; I was laughing because
I had acquired the true spirit of Plumhampton, I was a
parish priest at last.

2. The End of Brigid

Far be it for me to remind curates how lucky they
are or to ask of them more sympathy for their elders

and betters; at least they should note the endless frustration spared them on the kitchen front.

I, too, was heedless in my day. Curates may grumble about the food as did the Jews before them, but their share of the Manna turns up unfailingly four times a day. It is the parish priest who must wear the heavy mantle of Moses and even that great law-giver might well have found some housekeepers a strain. The curates stroll in, as often late as not, to partake of cottage pie and other delicacies, scarcely pausing to think that the pastor may have lain awake the night before wondering where that pie was coming from, and the night after pondering whence it had. Curates may share with the parish priest all the spiritual graces of the priesthood, but these do not include those gifts of wisdom, tact and blarney whereby a housekeeper is found, or stolen from a colleague, and then made holy enough to agree to remain.

The experienced pastor knows very well that if he is ever to be humble, firm, tolerant, prayerful and saintly, then his housekeeper will need the same virtues in double supply. So important is she to the running of a parish that Joe Plaster is prepared to place her above all the blessings in the *Ritual* and second only to the articles of the Creed.

Given a housekeeper as devoted as Nellie, the priest may turn his mind to the Lourdes pilgrimage, to novenas, missions, all-night vigils and similar luxuries. If the housekeeper is disgruntled, why the very form of the sacraments is threatened, for the priest has but half his mind on the baptismal water and the other half moving restlessly from the phone to the door bell, to the dinner, to the laundry, to the holes in his socks. Should there be no housekeeper at all, unmentionable things may happen as when two would-be converts, seeking instruction, shake hands with a priest who has forgotten that he is still carrying tomorrow's slab of cod.

I am able to write with particular feeling about this side of the pastor's worries, for, when I came to Plumhampton, the housekeeper left within a month. Such a general post is not uncommon after a change of Prime Minister, President or Parish Priest. Brigid was kindly enough, well-intentioned enough, but her heart was on the Shannon and that lovely river has an appeal which the Plumhampton canal could not supply. She did not leave in a hurry and there were moments, even consecutive days, when I thought that she might survive. I put up many candles, stuffed myself with her favourite dish, tinned ravioli, in the faint but unlikely hope that she might yet change her mind. We wavered, smiled, stared balefully at each other over each ravioli dish. Brigid, gazing at it, said that her work was too heavy; I, for other reasons, was inclined to agree. She finally left me for the Shannon and now writes wistfully of Plumhampton as though it had had for her all the glamour and wickedness of Soho.

When Brigid had gone, I reached the heroic decision to "do" for myself. Many parishioners offered to help, a rota of Children of Mary was prepared to provide my meals between them; such was the generosity of Plumhampton that I received eight fresh cauliflowers as presents on the very first day. But I was not yet sufficiently humble, learned, firm, tolerant, prayerful and saintly to want to be dependent on my parishioners. I felt that, with Children of Mary in my kitchen, today's nosegay might easily turn into tomorrow's thorns. Further, I found in myself the desire, at small cost, to appear heroic, a kind of Damian without lepers or Charles de Foucauld without sand. One had read so much about priest-workers in France and here was the very chance to win Plumhampton, to convert it, frying-pan in hand.

Switching on an inscrutable look and feeling like the Curé of Ars, back home and boiling his potatoes, I edged the Children of Mary from the kitchen and announced that I would "do" for myself for a few days. The searchers were out, the adverts were in all the Catholic papers and one could only hope and pray. A new housekeeper had to be found and, in the meantime, Joe Plaster offered to go half and half with his Teresa, he fasting on the odd, I on the even days.

3. PRIEST IN THE PANTRY

I "did" for myself for about ten days. I washed up, dried up, shut up, scoured the milk bottles and gazed at the gas cooker with an optimistic saucepan in my trembling hand. For the first few days I cooked in my cassock; later I was only prevented from wearing a bathing costume by the hot fat spitting from the pan. If this was not the image of myself that I had sought to create on arrival, it yet proved very effective and so impressed two lapsed Catholics that they resumed the practice of their faith. Plumhampton prayed for me and these prayers ascended to heaven like the smoke from the kipper fillets, left, inadvertently, under the grill.

I discovered why the Curé of Ars kept strictly to potatoes; I would have limited myself to nice, fresh lettuces from the garden if I could have found a way of getting the ants out of the house.

When the Council of the Church tackles the vexed question of seminary education, perhaps it will introduce a simple course of clerical cooking to balance the lectures of Dogma, Scripture and Philosophy. Thus would budding divines learn in practice as well as in theory all that is implied by the Incarnation and, also, by the Fall of Man. I could not help feeling that the laws of abstinence on Fridays would be speedily adjusted if the seminary professors had to get their own kipper fillets out of the neat-fitting polythene bag.

No, do not tell me! I, too, thought of my nail scissors and bounded to the bedroom with hope renewed. Back with the scissors, I found that the kippers had disappeared. They were not in the pantry, not in the bin, not with the tea leaves; I found them, later, lying quietly on my bed upstairs. After that, kipper fillets were erased from my menu; I could still smell them in the sacristy and confessional, having been with them throughout a restless night.

During the ten days of "doing" for myself, I formed certain clear resolutions which undoubtedly will be with me throughout my priestly life. I resolved never to start a service late or to preach for more than five minutes, seeing that more than half the congregation must rush home from church to prepare a meal. I further resolved to worry far less about books on sex and sex instruction when most of the problems of Christian marriage centre on the kitchen stove. I thought that, at the next pre-nuptial enquiry, I would enter the presbytery parlour wearing my biretta but with a frying-pan in my outstretched hand. I would say to the trembling groom, "Stop worrying about the other conditions, come with me to my kitchen and I will show you how to break an egg into a frying-pan." I resolved to have no pity at all on any disgruntled husband and to treat the new housekeeper, if and when I got her, with a reverence due to those who "do" for others as well as for themselves. Had I been cooking for others as well, and for those who grumbled, I would have passed from the Plumhampton presbytery to the Old Bailey with a twisted carver in my hand.

Before Nellie arrived to relieve me of a task ill-suited to Holy Orders, I had time to add one further simple resolution plus a rider condemning a certain type of parishioner. It happened like this. While I was still "doing" for myself, I decided to cook something very special to honour one of Our Lady's greater feasts. The sole in question was bought as a gift by the Children of Mary, washed by the Catholic Women's League, arranged and blessed by the Union of Catholic Mothers and steamed by me, the parish priest. My lovely fresh sole rested happily between two plates above a boiling saucepan with egg sauce, veg. and milk simmering on either side. I was standing back exultantly, experiencing the proud feelings of the discoverer of Penicillin when the telephone rang.

The enquirer was not known to me but she wanted to know the times for confession and entered into a very lengthy explanation of the reasons which prevented her coming at the various official times. Even the Curé of Ars might have been a little testy had he been steaming his first piece of fresh sole. With my ear to one soul and my eye on the other, I begged the would-be penitent to come at any hour of the day or night. I would have absolved her over the phone, had the *Clergy Review* allowed it, to get back to my steaming sole in time.

In trying to end the conversation I had, clearly, been too gushing; my round-the-clock invitation provoked further confidences. My unknown client told me that her husband was this, her children that, her own parish priest the other, but that as a good Catholic she intended to bear her cross in silence and to say no more about such things. For most priests, this last expression has an ominous ring.

"Quite right," said I, with mounting panic. "Any time, any day, ta-ta, bye-bye; God bless; don't mention," and I replaced the receiver with alacrity. Racing to the gas cooker, I felt a twinge of pious envy; Our Lady had no telephone at Nazareth.

All seemed well with my many pots and pans, and

yet this was the very moment at which a simple course of clerical cooking would have proved most useful, especially if given by a professor with true pastoral experience.

The phone rang again. I may now admit quite simply that I lost my supper because I lost my head.

Yes, it was the same caller again, with one more teeny-weeny question; if she came to confession on a Thursday, could she count it for the First Friday as well?

She, too, must have heard the muffled crash in the kitchen followed by my cry of pain.

"I did not quite catch, Father," said she.

"No, nor did I," I returned tartly—a remark that Manning, Knox, Heenan or Ripley would never have made. It was after this that I decided to cut any parishioner who phones just before dinner and, further, never to cry over spilt sole, veg. sauce—and, of course, milk!

Happily Nellie arrived within three days.

4. NELLIE

A great number of people took the credit to themselves for finding Nellie, but I have to regard her as an answer to my harassed prayers. In fact, she had just buried a dear old canon from some Midlands parish for whom she had been keeping house for years. She was led by grace to read my advertisement in the Catholic papers and made the same mistake about Plumhampton that I had made myself. She pictured a thatched presbytery near to a yew-shaded churchyard, a parish with no bingo and a house with few stairs.

Nellie was middle-aged, neat, motherly and portly, four foot ten inches in her slippers and with greying hair. She came originally from Northumberland, had spent her years in many different cities, had no official spiritual life but said many prayers. She is not fussy about dogma, is not much worried about salvation,

presumes that every priest is holy, loves all the saints in heaven and Doctor Kildare. Nellie is wholly in-different to food, board or hours, takes fresh air and exercise when she goes out shopping, reads every word of every Catholic paper carefully. In a motherly way she is partial to young men. She thinks that all altar boys have priestly vocations but her attitude is more complex as regard to nuns. Of course, she has, in theory, a great devotion to all the dear sisters, but the grudge against Sister St Vincent has clouded her judgment for thirty years.

Indeed, Nellie came to me with three clear prejudices which were fully disclosed inside a week. She held that

Ushaw College was the only seminary in England, that Our Lord and His mother wanted her to win at bingo and that Sister St Vincent had borrowed her hoover and refused to give it back. A priest who might hope to hold Nellie's loyalty had to accept these facts.

It cost me nothing to accept that Ushaw was the only seminary in England in return for Nellie's delicious liver and bacon or a steamed sole for old times' sake. Sensitive theologians would no doubt have fallen back on a *restrictio late mentalis* but, frankly, I would have razed our seminary to the ground rather than have to cook again. Nellie has given me potted biographies of many past presidents of Ushaw and, though I admit to feeling guilty, I have always made cooing noises and dutifully nodded my head. I feel sure that Manning, Knox, Heenan and Ripley, faced with the loss of Nellie's liver and bacon, would do the same.

Sister St Vincent and the hoover is a more complicated story, but Nellie needs no answer and only tells it when she is feeling generally depressed. For weeks on end I hear nothing of poor Sister St Vincent and then I have her dastardly deed with all its perfidious details for three consecutive days. Sister St Vincent's sin was committed thirty years ago. Nellie had lent her presbytery hoover to the convent for the Prize Day at the canon's express request. She had warned him but he would not listen, so she personally had carried it across. She had watched her hoover from a distance as the mother of Moses had watched the hazards of her infant son. Nellie seems to have known in advance what was going to happen and it did. When she asked for her hoover back, she was told that it belonged to the convent and, in proof of this assertion, she was shown the inscription "St Teresa's Dorm." written across the canvas with white paint. When she told the canon, he went out at once and bought her another, not wanting to lose his liver and bacon and anxious above all to keep the peace. Nellie maintains to this day that Sister St Vincent, if not Reverend Mother, used that white paint to hide the truth. Nellie always ends by saying, "Now that kind of deceit could never have happened at Ushaw," and once again, without qualm, I nod my head.

The third prejudice, bingo, is a real temptation, perhaps the only real temptation in Nellie's selfless life. Indeed she tells me that she chose Plumhampton to break the habit just as an alcoholic chooses some quiet home. It came as a shock to Nellie when she reached Plumhampton to find a Bingo Palace further down the road.

Nellie never wins at bingo but she feels that she has it in her and that heaven is on her side. She goes to bingo twice a week, once out of loyalty to our parish orgy, once to Royal Bingo at the Palace to which all the gamblers of Plumhampton flock. On these bingo nights, Nellie says her rosary early and invokes an exceptional number of saints. One can tell at midday that the fever is in her blood again. By 7 p.m. Nellie is getting ready and reciting her last-minute prayers. If she ever wins a large sum of money, she will certainly send the lot to Ushaw; it is this bribe that she uses when praying to the Northumbrian saints.

My only small tiff with Nellie hinged on bingo and it was typical of her that our row should be based on her unselfishness. About a month after she had come, I

inadvertently forgot that Wednesday was her Royal
Bingo evening and invited Joe Plaster and two others
to a meal. When I told Nellie of this arrangement, she
said nothing but her face fell. I immediately corrected
the mistake. I said that Joe Plaster could as easily change
to another evening, but Nellie would not hear of this.
I insisted and she resisted, remarking again and again
with all the determination of a past president of Ushaw,
"No, certainly not."

The battle of the bingo lasted for several days. Nellie
was coldly polite to me but without relenting, I, on
the other hand, was fatherly but firm. Indeed I went so
far as to cancel the supper engagement and to tell Nellie
so. Nellie received the news as a martyr might have
heard from the royal palace a final offer of reprieve.

We may never know how the matter was settled,
but the answer was an answer to prayer. I knew very
well that Nellie was saying rosary after rosary in the
kitchen, not for her bingo but for me. I, too, put up
many a candle and recited the *De Profundis* as I took
down and dusted my one and only cookery book.

Nellie now says that she had determined not to go to
the bingo that Wednesday evening but that the craving
overcame her at the end. As the clock moved round to
7.30 p.m. she could not stop herself. She went. When
I heard the door bang, I could not easily tell whether or
not I would ever see her again.

Nellie was back at 10.30 p.m. and, miracle of miracles,
she had won at bingo for the only time in her blameless
life. It would be nice to record that she had won a
hoover to snub Sister St Vincent, but she sent her
10s. 6d. to Ushaw; a small ad. "In thanksgiving to St

Cuthbert" appeared the next week in the *Universe*. I
believe secretly that it was St Gertrude and that tomorrow's nosegay was mine at last.

5. THE BEGGARS' OPERA

In the first days and weeks of my stay in Plumhampton, my former fellow curates were in terrifying
form. They phoned every day to frolic, sent me anonymous letters, recommended both beggars and commer-
cial travellers to try my door. I was offered family
Bibles of every size, a water softener of a type used in
three Anglican cathedrals, a lounge suit with adjustable
fittings which could be let out if I, later, became a
prelate or dean. I myself had been a curate and knew
that time alone would effect a cure.

Aften ten days, the curate menace abated but the
beggars took its place. The curates might phone twice
a week to ask after my spiritual welfare while the
beggars rang the doorbell every day. Here is a serious
threat to a one-priest mission; few priests are gifted
enough to answer the doorbell and persuade an ex-
pectant beggar that the priest is not at home. Joe Plaster
recommends a hideous mask from the local toy-shop; he
says that the one of the devil has often proved effective,
especially with the Irish and the Poles.

When I became a parish priest, I made a secret resolution to deal with all beggars by myself. After all, it was
my responsibility, my money, my vocation, nor could
I wholly disregard the example of the saints. These holy
men were for ever putting chaps to bed, washing their
wounds, tending their sores, nourishing their bodies; I,
too, would have liked to copy St Martin of Tours in

generosity but my cheap clerical raincoat would have
served no useful purpose to either of us if, in a burst of
fervour, I had slit it in two.

After a fortnight in Plumhampton I knew, what I
had long suspected, that I lacked the personal magnetism
peculiar to the saints. I had magnetism of a sort, for all
the beggars were attracted to me, but this was not
holiness in the full Thurston-Butler sense. No Plumhampton beggar would have changed his life or blessed
me had I dumped him in my bed. Again, few of the
Plumhampton beggars had sores to which I could attend.
All to a man turned up their noses at cold bread-and-

butter pudding; they simply ignored it and began their
rigmarole again.

They would show me documents galore, pictures of
the Sacred Heart, certificates of confirmation in part ex-

planation of their need for cash. I listened to countless happy reminiscences about dear old Ireland, the sweet sisters of Kilkenny, dear old Fr O'Casey, chaplain of the Dublin Fusiliers. From whatever part of the world they had come, their mother's dying words remained to haunt them, "Promise me, son, that whenever you are in trouble, you will go at once to the dear, kind, holy priest." All my beggars had proved filial at least in this.

Otherwise their stories varied though their need was the same. Almost all had been discharged from hospital with ulcers, had a definite job in Newquay if they could only get their bag of tools from Ipswich for which they required the cloakroom fee. Most had not eaten for a fortnight and had a wife and six young children to maintain. When I mentioned bread-and-butter pudding, some of them cried a little as though, rather than suffer such humiliation, they would like their wife and kiddies to follow them to a pauper's grave.

In my curate days, we all faced this same problem but the cash was not ours to give. We could afford to weep quietly with each new beggar and refer him kindly to the parish priest. Now I was a parish priest. Now it was not so easy to face God boldly after sending these, his little ones, away. At the same time it was clearly impossible to part with non-existent funds.

My former fellow curates used to assert that a teeny-weeny lie on such occasions is morally justified in self-defence. It was their contention that the battle is lost just as soon as the priest listens and that attack is the one sure line of escape. Fr Soap took the more aggressive approach, staring at the beggar before demanding in a voice of thunder, "My man, are you a good, practising Catholic?" To the invariable answer, he would reply with vigour, "Well, I am not!" Soap says that the *Clergy Review* seemed to agree with his solution, but had warned him not to take Matthew 19.17 in too rabbinical a sense.

Fr O'Flaherty, on the other hand, chose the more pitiful approach. Running to the door and obviously short of breath, he would gasp to each beggar, "Thank God, you've come, man. I have six monsignori upstairs dying of cholera!" Apparently the *Clergy Review* is also prepared to back O'Flaherty, following the Jesuit Moral Theologians, provided that he uses "upstairs" in a sense *late mentalis* and does not imply by word or gesture that all six monsignori are in the same room. O'Flaherty has found that cholera sounds better than whooping-cough or measles and that "quicker than the second collection" the beggar has gone.

The above are merely curates' solutions, a parish priest has his soul to save. He must be as firm as any curate or ruin will stretch before him, but he must also be discreet. The *Clergy Review* quotes a reply of the Sacred Congregation on the careful use of parish money in which Rome answers the question about gifts and donations with the clear ruling *Videtur quod Non*.

As a parish priest I have found that the easiest way to deal with beggars is to organize a "crow's nest" on the landing or in an upstairs room. Breviary, shot gun and holy water are optional advantages, the one essential is a good view of the front door. Next, when the bell rings, one takes a look, descends to the lower floor, signals for Nellie and indicates to her by signs from

behind the coat rack that the parish priest is away
making his retreat. Nellie is four foot ten, with a
motherly way about her, tons of cold bread-and-butter
pudding and, of course, no cash. Further, she is lucky;
not having studied theology she sees no reason to seek
the support of the *Clergy Review*.

It was Nellie's success which provided the germ of
lasting solution which I discussed with Joe Plaster some
months ago. We were compelled to agree that Nellie,
like St Martin of Tours, was saved by her secular dress.
We had to accept that it is the Roman collar which
betrays the priest. Each beggar takes us for a sucker and
knows very well that if he goes on long enough about
his First Communion day in dear old Ireland eventually
we will be paying for him to go to Ipswich to collect his
tools. Granted a Roman collar, one is eventually forced
to turn the other cheek. Joe Plaster asserts that the
Clergy Review had more or less anticipated our question with a most encouraging article on clerical dress.
Though normally a priest must dress in his clerical
outfit, yet all the Doctors and Congregations make the
distinction that certain situations demand a more apt
form of dress. Barbarini-Fizz gives the very telling
situation in which a Domestic Prelate, going by lifeboat
to the aid of a man who has fallen from a trawler near
Iceland, need not wear a purple stock. We, in open
shirts, wearing cricket caps, toying with a golf club,
would have every beggar guessing from the start.

Joe promised to write to the *Clergy Review* for a
general comment but, luckily, I was able to see the flaw
in time. For when the door bell rang yesterday and I
from my watch-tower had inspected the back of the

typically seedy raincoat, I decided to give the Plaster
gambit a trial. "Leave it to me," said I to Nellie, and
removed my Roman collar hurriedly. Nellie for once
looked a little surprised. I, too, felt a qualm and a little
foolish but there was no shirking now. I laid hold of a
cloth cap, left behind by my predecessor, and grabbed
the pair of binoculars from the sitting-room. The Domestic Prelate on his sea voyage to Iceland looked no more
strange than I. Happily, at the very last moment, I
rejected Fr Soap's beginning; it would have added insult
to injury had I put the question, "My man, are you a
good practising Catholic?" to the austere Canon Bear-
man, diocesan promoter of the fund for distressed
clergy, whom I found standing at my door.

No beggar could have looked more surprised than
did the canon. "Ah, Father," said he without warmth.
"I hardly recognized you. I called to find out how you
were faring, but, well, there is no need to worry, you
have obviously settled down."

6. THE GENERAL

To present a complete picture of those first hectic
days in my new parish, I dare not omit the General.
The martial presence of this remarkable man may serve
to correct an otherwise wrong impression that parish
life in Plumhampton was one long hysterical laugh. The
General did not laugh. He had an attitude to God so
realistic and ruthlessly objective that he not only
brought the altar boys to their senses but even pulled
me up with a jerk.

The first Sunday for a new parish priest proves a
momentous occasion, for on that day, for the first time,

he meets his flock. He prays with them, blesses them, notes their idiosyncrasies and customs, with them offers Mass for their good estate. A new parish priest may often be placed at a disadvantage, for he is a complete stranger, knowing no names, unsure of local procedure, not too certain of the keys and cupboards, very afraid to betray himself. He may not fully approve of all that his predecessor has permitted but he must seem to accept that this is the perfect parish and must keep his misgivings to himself. He may find the alb too short, the altar steps too narrow, the notes provided by the organist far too high for his very limited voice. To attempt such notes, as I did, only to find oneself screeching like a cock on a spring morning, is to risk depression and a sense of failure which may last for months.

On that first Sunday, I knew only Frank Shaw, an admirable young student from the Plumhampton Polytechnic, for Frank had called to introduce himself the night before. Frank was one of those who smile much, work hard and say little, on whom my predecessor had relied for more or less everything. Mutual shyness prevented deep or personal conversation and we spoke solemnly for seven minutes about keys.

It was Frank who first told me about the General; he said, in an offhand manner, "The General takes the thurible." Naturally I presumed that "the General" was a nickname, for one meets so many of those to whom God has given a face or figure which earns for them such titles as the Squire, the General or the Duke. Frank put me right on this, for our thurifer was a true General, though Frank, at twenty, was young enough to be hazy about dates. El Alamein meant little to

Frank. He thought that our general had won the D.S.O.
or something, had been in the Tank Corps, or something, was a convert from something, and so on. For
Frank, a student at the Polytechnic, the General was
important chiefly as thurifer.

I met the General in the sacristy before the second
Mass. If I was all at sea, he, too, should have been feeling
much embarrassed, for he had squeezed his bulk into a
black, ill-fitting cassock, topped by a cotta first designed
for a slight boy of fourteen. The General's gold cuff-
links first caught my eye, for he had more than the
liturgical length of shirt protruding from the cassock's
inadequate sleeves. The General was slightly flushed in
the face, for he must have found it hard to breathe. Yet
he seemed entirely at home, unembarrassed, friendly
with the altar boys who pushed around him, like tugs
easing a Cunarder out of Southampton docks.

No need for me to emphasize the virtue of the
General, his very presence was a tonic to my harassed
soul. During the Sung Mass itself, the thurifer added
considerably to both the dignity and gaiety of the Plumhampton rite. The General was in deadly earnest and
the altar boys, as always eager to find an excuse for
laughter, respected him too much even to smile.

He carried the thurible smartly, as they might have
done at Sandhurst, but when he swung it, he might have
been lobbing a grenade into an enemy tank. When the
chains of the thurible were recalcitrant, he said, "Oh
bother"; at the Offertory his language was scriptural
and stronger, but the choir drowned it as they charged
with vigour at their second verse.

After Mass the General, in tweeds and slacks, offered

me a welcome, shaking my hand in a grip which nearly snapped my fingers and giving his name as Starch. He added no prefix, just a simple invitation that I would let him know at once if he or his wife could be of any help.

A parish priest would be a saint if he learned from his mistakes. Too anxious to please, too subjective, too on edge, not on familiar terms with Generals, I erred in thanking him humbly for coming to act as thurifer.

The General stood back, shaken and dismayed. "Damn it all, Padre," he said, "you mustn't thank me. What would you say if I thanked you for offering Mass? I love it. Who cares about the cassock? You and I are doing this for God."

The General rarely appears in this Plumhampton story. He made it very clear to me that he regarded the service of the altar as the best and only way for him in serving God. But, from time to time, I would sit and talk with him in his home over a glass of whiskey: he never mentioned El Alamein, only God. He always has his whiskey. As he said to me once, "It used to be half a bottle, but now that I have discovered Lourdes Water, I am happy with a double Scotch."

Chapter Three

NUNMANSHIP

NEW PARISH PRIESTS, I was warned, when first they reach their new presbyteries, hardly give themselves enough time to mislay their breviaries before they are off to greet the nuns. Very right that they should. They know which side their bread is buttered and that any plans not backed by Reverend Mother will wither as the grass.

I, too, was off to the convent at the first opportunity, for had not Reverend Mother welcomed me with a significant text. Beautifully inscribed on parchment were these words from Isaias: "Before they call, I shall answer; while they are yet speaking, I will hear" (65.24). This cryptic message called for meditation later; for the moment, in a roundabout way, the prophet counselled speed.

45

As I steered my Austin through Plumhampton's residential quarter, I sensed that Reverend Mother from her prie-dieu or watch-tower was, somehow, following

me. Strange things have happened to priests who fall under the spell of Reverend Mothers—either they are raised on high as in the days of the great St Teresa or sideways, like Fr James Frick, late of our diocese, who ended his days in a rest home to the north of Waterford. No, I was not frightened, only careful; while I was yet speaking, Reverend Mother could already hear.

At first there seemed small cause for care. Reverend Mother was short, graceful, gracious and soft-spoken, with a deeply spiritual sense of humour and, I imagine, with a merry twinkle in her eye. I could not see this last for my own eyes were modestly lowered, while Reverend Mother had received a habit from her foundress which made her look like a photographer crouching and waiting for the little birdie to appear.

Reverend Mother was courtesy itself. She showed me part of her lovely school without forcing me into every classroom, spoke a little of her Mother Foundress but kept something back for another time. She mentioned my predecessor with such a perfect blend of charity and wisdom that I could feel myself a definite improvement on him without forming too flattering a view of myself. She certainly never said that the bishop called to consult her on grave educational matters but one was led to deduce that a wise and holy bishop often would.

Reverend Mother grew more and more cryptic as our tour continued and I came to suspect that, like Isaias, she had a further, hidden message to convey. Only on parting, and out of the blue, did she pop the question; how nice it would be, she thought, if I would sing the High Mass, next Monday, in the convent chapel, when dear Mother Assistant would be keeping her golden jubilee.

"While she was yet speaking, I could hear." At once and ill prepared, I found myself faced with a loaded question, for no Reverend Mother discloses all her demands at once. I had to make a choice. Was Reverend Mother working on the principle, "If the worst comes to the worst, we can always ask the parish," or had she said to the happy jubilarian, "We had better ask the parish first; you know very well, Mother, how touchy they can be!"

Mine proved an inspired guess. When I asked to be excused on the grounds that I was new to Plumhampton and that my ceremonies were rusty, Reverend Mother readily agreed. She added for good measure that she often wondered how a parish priest coped with the work that came his way. She would pray that God would give me strength. It was agreed between us that she would find the celebrant for the Jubilee Mass from another source.

I was already in my car with the engine ticking over when Reverend Mother stepped forward with a further request. She felt that the community would be hurt if the parish priest was not with them for the great occasion so, perhaps, I would act as subdeacon and stay for luncheon afterwards. After all, the subdeacon did very little and was only required to stand still.

Not having Manning, Knox, Heenan or Ripley at hand to help me, I surrendered and agreed to her plan. "Splendid," said Reverend Mother, and one felt that she was smiling because the little birdie had worked. "You'll act as subdeacon," she said, "and we'll ask the Abbot of Pudsey to sing the Mass while dear Father Allsop, the Jesuit, can be deacon and preach. Our own dear chaplain is, alas, not up to it." I had been had. And it was no use praying to our parish patroness, St Gertrude, for she, too, had been a Reverend Mother in her day.

I drove home with a coloured brochure about the convent school on the seat beside me and a very slight irritation in my heart. The convent motto—I could read it on the cover—ran: *Tuto Tela Servate*, which Joe Plaster, later, rendered roughly: "Sisters, keep your powder dry."

Yes, I made a splendid subdeacon, standing very still. At lunch, while Reverend Mother talked to Fr Abbot, I found myself one place lower down the table than dear Fr Allsop, the Jesuit. I was near enough to drop a hint to him that he might like to give a mission in my humble church. As a good Jesuit, Fr Allsop replied that there was literally nothing that he would like better and that he would make a note about the dates. But, he thought, perhaps, that he ought to finish his doctorate thesis first. Yes, after eighteen years he was still studying for God's greater glory, his subject at the moment, "The reproductive cycle in certain warm-water fish."

When I remarked that I did not know that the message of the Incarnation had to be preached to fishes, dear Fr Allsop joined in the joke. He thought that Holy Obedience came before preaching and that the Church should keep her tail up even in the world of fish !

Reverend Mother could not express her thanks enough, as she assured me on departure; she felt that I had the true spirit of her foundress and that she and I would work together as devoted friends.

Just a week after I had hauled down my flag and taken my place as subdeacon, Reverend Mother sent me a charming little note. She opened by asking if there was anything that the community could do to help me, for though they did not see as much of me as they would like, having, as they have, a resident chaplain, yet I was, in the full sense, their pastor, always to the fore in their heartfelt prayers. Reverend Mother went on to say that she would presume in me the same affection and would I do them a small favour in return. She had Dom Heinrich Söndermann staying at the convent and it would help her greatly if I would invite him to lunch one day. It was hardly necessary, she thought, to remind me that Dom Heinrich was a world-famous expert on the Minor Prophets, for, certainly, I would be familiar with his books. Dom Heinrich was over in England for a rest. Reverend Mother described him as a dear, kind soul who had already helped the headmistress in the correct interpretation of certain catechetical texts. Dom Heinrich had many times expressed the wish to meet some of his fellow priests. She felt sure that he had problems to discuss which no nuns would understand!

I was a little flustered and not a little flattered; if it was a great honour for the Plumhampton presbytery to entertain so great a scholar, I had to admit that I had never even heard of Dom Heinrich or read any of his books. Still I was hardly in the position to refuse a visit and consulted Brigid, who was still with me, to arrange a satisfying lunch. Brigid thought that foreigners would like nothing so much as ravioli, seeing that it came from their part of the world.

When Dom Heinrich appeared, he proved to be the kind of "dear" that Reverend Mother had described. He was very charming, very humble, anxious to practise his excellent English at any cost. He spoke very loud and clear with some of the resonance of a Minor Prophet; he told me about them from the very start. He said, "Oh, no, no!", and laughed uproariously when I offered him whiskey—then remarked, "There is no changing of the English is there?" and, finally, helped himself to a small tot. The prophets Amos and Osee, wise men of their generation, would hardly have taken less. Nevertheless, the whiskey proved just enough to remove any lingering inhibitions and Dom Heinrich gave me a most interesting lecture on Osee 5.8.

I can hardly blame him, for I it was who started him off. When I remarked that I was deeply interested in the Minor Prophets, he answered with index finger raised, "Oh, ho, Reverend Mother has told me," and then he was under starter's orders and off. "Blow ye the cornet in Gibeah and the trumpet in Ramah" was the verse which had been holding him up for months. He suggested, purely as an hypothesis, that we must both be prepared to accept the fact that Osee used the word "trumpet" in an wholly exceptional sense. Dom Heinrich described to me various kinds of trumpets, including the one which Osee had probably in mind. Indeed, Dom Heinrich was actually blowing an imaginary Assyrian trumpet when his eye fell on my bookshelf with its sad assortment of pamphlets and paperbacks. He wondered if I had handy Stömpf's *Alttestamentliche-blasinstrumentengeschichte*, Vol. 26?

I was tempted to reply that I had lent that particular volume to the housekeeper for her spiritual reading but, somehow, I lacked the heart. Dom Heinrich was so kind, so earnest, so absorbed in his work. Further, though puzzled, I was also flattered that he should speak so openly about Osee's trumpet as though he and I and the Minor Prophet were old friends. Dom Heinrich stayed for three hours and thanked me most cordially at the end. He promised to return on some future occasion to discuss the exact location of Gibeah.

Dom Heinrich's behaviour became very much clearer three days later, when Emily, the maid from the convent, called at our presbytery. She was friendly with

Brigid and often came to our kitchen for a chat. On
this occasion she told Brigid, quite innocently, that Dom
Heinrich had not wanted to go out to lunch that day
—he was busy writing—but that Reverend Mother had

persuaded him. Reverend Mother had told him in
Emily's presence that the parish priest had specially
invited him to lunch. She had urged him to go "because
the poor parish clergy have so few chances of contact
with scholars; our own parish priest is deeply interested
in the Minor Prophets and a visit from the great Dom
Heinrich might improve his sermons enormously."

There was still one piece missing to the Dom Heinrich story and dear Sister Rogatian, the portress at the
convent, provided this. Sister Rogatian, sweet soul that
she is, thanked me so warmly on my next visit to the
convent, for, if I had not taken Dom Heinrich off their
hands on that occasion, Mother Assistant could never
have had the full celebration of her jubilee. The nuns
had only the one parlour now that the others had been
turned into piano cells for the school. Dom Heinrich

was firmly established and while he continued to play his cornet in Gibeah, Mother Assistant could not sound her trumpet in Ramah as she should.

Sister Rogatian described to me how the sisters, the moment Dom Heinrich had left for lunch, removed all the Minor Prophets from the parlour to give Mother Assistant her first real break in fifty years. Reverend Mother had told the community to pray hard while she tried to fix things; thanks to me, their prayer had been answered and she had.

How could I feel the slightest grievance against Reverend Mother who spent her life trying to please others as I did myself? I felt nothing but a mounting sympathy. But I made a mental note to consult the approved authors, to pray for Reverend Mother to St Gertrude and, in the meantime, to keep my powder dry.

The final part of the second leg of my tie with Reverend Mother turned on the parish First Communion day. Here was my first chance as a parish priest to attempt some liturgical improvement and I wanted to make the most of it. Plumhampton, I knew, would respond most generously. The teachers drew up the list of names, we ran special catechism classes, parents bought bales of white material, flowers were promised from every side.

If Plumhampton was to become the parish I longed for it to be, then we must arrange a First Communion breakfast after Mass was over, as a practical sign of our charity. Never before in Plumhampton had there been a proposal for such a meal. In preparation for it, I preached two earnest sermons on the ancient Christian love-feast or Agape. The professor of Church history at the seminary sounded startled when I phoned to know if any liturgical Mrs Beaton from an earlier century had recorded the correct menu for such a meal. The professor, after some thought, favoured fish and honey as being scriptural but agreed that neither was very suitable with kids. In the end, it was agreed that eggs and bacon, parochially subscribed to and publicly eaten by the children, would be a fit symbol of charity. Here, for me, was the kernel of the liturgical mustard seed. The liturgy will only thrive in a happy family and my children were jolly well going to love each other even if they were all sick for a week.

Just a week before the Agape and Communion celebration, a note came from the convent with many mystic letters and *"et Maria"* at the top of the page. Reverend Mother was saddened and alarmed. She feared that, through her fault, there had been a misunderstanding, for she should have informed me of Plumhampton's liturgical ways. My much loved predecessor had agreed that the convent children should make their First Communion at school. She reckoned this a very fair decision for they should receive Our Lord for the first time with their school friends all around them and in the place that was the centre of their little world. Reverend Mother felt sure that I, who had quickly caught the spirit of their holy foundress, would show myself once more as the convent's greatest friend.

For the very first time since my seminary days when, as an accolyte, I had set fire to the subdeacon, I found myself uncertain of myself. One half urged fight to assert the central position of the parish, the other half told me not to be silly, for only one child was involved. Maudie was our only First Communicant this year who went to school at the convent and it would be stupid to have a dispute about her. My first half disagreed because, in a liturgical parish, there should be none of these spiritual class distinctions, the nuns and all their children should come to the First Communion Mass and to the Communion breakfast at the parish church. My second half, facetiously, then called to mind a dictum of my irresponsible, former fellow curates, "Farewell to the purple stock, old boy, if you offend the old girl."

While I was thus struggling in my soul—at lunch I had sent back the ravioli untasted to the kitchen—Joe Plaster and Vincent Apse were knocking at my door. Joe Plaster was furious and Vincent Apse was more than mildly annoyed. The Reverend Mother of Mulberry-under-Trill was also threatening to steal five First Communicants, three from Joe Plaster's parish and two from Vin's. Joe said that he was merely calling in for my prayers and blessing on his way to the airport for he intended to put the whole matter before the appropriate pontifical congregation in Rome. He would not be surprised if, after he had laid his case before it, the Congregation did not put Reverend Mother and her community under an interdict. In the good old days they would have been burned at the stake. Fr Apse, a convert Anglican monk, was slightly more moderate, praying secretly to the Holy Spirit to help dear Reverend Mother to see sense. Surely she could see that because a school is independent and fee-paying, it is not entitled to be exclusive in the administration of the sacraments.

To me, who had not yet disclosed my hand or my present situation, they both looked so funny that I feared I might start to laugh. Vin Apse kept muttering to himself, "Twenty-five years in the one true Church and now a tiff with the dear sisters," or, alternatively, "Oh dear, I never feel happy riding my high horse." Joe Plaster rounded on him, "Don't be silly, Vin, in a skirmish with Reverend Mother, you'd be far safer on a giraffe."

I could contain myself no longer and started to laugh. Joe Plaster was very angry, told me to control myself, that this was no laughing matter, that the whole parochial life of England, established in the sixth century by St Theodore of Tarsus, was being gnawed away by nuns. Vin Apse made it funnier still by intervening in a whisper, "Don't want to correct you, Joe, but Theodore of Tarsus lived in the seventh century."

When they left me, Joe Plaster was still riding his giraffe. He had not laughed. I, who had, could no longer continue my resistance, for laughter is the death of pride in all its forms. I wrote a charming letter to Reverend Mother, outlining my liturgical aspirations for the parish, the mind of the Pope, the plans for the Communion breakfast, the need to bring all the children together, and their parents, but in such personal and sacred matters I would like to leave all free to choose. If Maudie wanted to make her First Communion at the convent, she certainly could.

I knew very well that Maudie did not care a hoot. She chose the parish because Reverend Mother put it in her mind to do so and our Agape was thus complete. Further, when I came to vest for the First Communion Mass, I found a fine, white chasuble on the vesting table. Bottom centre, in fine gold thread, was the convent motto, *Tuto Tela Servate*; I had kept my powder dry.

When I phoned Joe Plaster to tell him about the gift of vestments, he became more angry than before. No, his First Communicants had gone to the convent and all that he had had was an illuminated card. "As a matter of fact," said Joe, "they sent me the motto of their flipping convent, *Una Semper atque Supra*, which may be roughly rendered, 'One up to Us'."

Chapter Four

THE TRUTH ABOUT YOUTH

WHEN Frs Joe Plaster and Vincent Apse are together, theirs is always a very amusing turn. So it was even at the seminary. The patter is not rehearsed nor their humour studied; both stem from the contrasting qualities of these two great friends. If one may hardly compare them to Martha and Mary, they are, at least, as different as Gothic and Baroque.

Vin Apse has always moved in a "Cloud of Unknowing" while Joe Plaster is more *Clergy Review*. Says Joe, "I simply cannot understand, Vin, why you chose the poor, benighted, secular clergy, when you could have gone the whole hog and taken the veil at Lisieux." Vin Apse, on the other hand, addressed me with all solemnity on another occasion: "Father, one s-simply must accept s-s-some simple theory of evolution; Joe

58

Plaster cannot be going to s-stop as he is for eternity?"

Their methods of prayer are different, too, for Vin Apse always prays with the Psalmist—"who am I, old man, to try to improve on the Holy S-Spirit?"—while Joe Plaster once tossed off this prayer in a moment of exasperation: "Lord, I am a swine, as well thou knowest," which must have brought the house down in Paradise.

Vincent Apse is parish priest of St Osmund's, Little Buckle, a parish which adjoins my northern frontier and meets Joe Plaster's in the south. Vin's was a late vocation; he had in his day been a bus conductor and then an Anglican monk. How he survived the seminary training was a miracle to all his friends. He seemed too absent-minded, genteel and frail to last the course. He came through with no more than a flickering eyelid and a very slight stutter, counterbalanced by an infectious love of God. We all presumed that he would end his days as chaplain to a quiet community of contemplatives but, believe it or not, he is now recognized in our diocese as a leading expert on Youth.

He enters my story at this point because of all my problems in Plumhampton, none is more worrying than the Youth. When I came to Plumhampton a year ago, I was faced with many headaches, the liturgy, the debt, the choir, the school, the roof and the headmistress, plus, in capital letters, The Youth. Given a little patience, all the other questions seem soluble, though, looking back, few are yet completely solved. On the Youth front, one is able to see no solution, for the Church, on the parochial level, finds it hard to pick up the wavelength of the teenage world. My predecessor had taken the cynical, possibly sensible line, "Ah, to be sure, what's all this blather? They won't be teenagers for more than ten years."

Plumhampton boasted a Youth Club of sorts, that is an Army hut on the far side of the church. We had two table-tennis sets and a battered dartboard on which some humorist had chalked an impression of the last parish priest. Our club also housed the Pascal Candlestick when out of season, stacks of old music and a drum used for mixing raffle tickets at the garden fête. Over the door Cardinal Godfrey gazed down without obvious approval through a battered piece of cellophane.

Our Youth Club leader, Mr Stephen Mantrip, had worked in Uganda and was always game for a lantern lecture on the Dutch missions and their sterling work. Mrs Begorrah, Mrs Murphy and Miss Anstey had been many times to that. Now retired, Mr Mantrip came to the club three days a week to teach knots, first-aid and cooking to a dwindling but enthusiastic group of cubs. He took them bird-spotting when weather and season allowed. Four older boys dropped into the club on occasion but they had other views about bird-spotting and spent their time combing their hair and running through the list of local girls. Politely they saluted me as "Father" but gazed at me pityingly.

A private opinion poll, conducted by myself throughout Plumhampton, disclosed the painful truth. My most active and devoted parishioners who would do anything for the Pope, the sick, the poor, the suffering, were quite out of sympathy with Youth. The General, certainly, had the secret, and the altar boys loved him, but he, good man, confined his attention only to the liturgy.

For a new parish priest, it is hard to avoid an idealized impression of Youth. One comes to believe that somewhere there is a fine young man, half Joan of Arc, half St Michael, who is panting to search for the Holy Grail before turning his horse's head towards the seminary. For Nellie and all the rest, Youth is always brought down to three dimensions, the altar boys who flick candle wax at each other, or the tedious boy next door. All the grown-ups at Plumhampton feel that young men have far too much pocket-money and that it is unfair to burden the parish by subscribing for further fun and games.

Of course Reverend Mother and the Community saw things very differently and they would do all that they could for the young. After all, had not Mother Foundress once whispered, "Sisters, what could I not do if you would bring me back my Youth?" The nuns were most generous in the loan of the convent hall. At the same time, I could hardly expect them to surrender all the prayer and quiet of their religious life. Teenagers in Plumhampton, as elsewhere, only really get started at 10.30 p.m. By that time the Community is fast asleep. Again, one cannot run a successful dance without smoking or if girls are forbidden to wear stiletto heels. Reverend Mother was with me in all this but she is not free to change the constitutions, and the next General Chapter meets in Rome in 1975. Reverend Mother believes that we may see many sensational changes then. In the meantime, she had promised to pray for our Plumhampton Youth Work, and in return, would we send to the convent the well-mannered and rather more affluent girls?

The situation seemed so desperate—one sees so few of the teenagers in church on Sundays—that I decided to call on Joe Plaster at Mulberry-under-Trill. Joe has his limitations but he is recognized in our diocese as an expert on more or less everything.

I had only to utter the word "Youth" for Joe Plaster's eyes to grow wide with pleasure, like the eyes of a child watching a Punch and Judy show. "Youth," he repeated; "Brother, lead me to them," and he escorted me to the well-filled bookcase lining one wall of his sitting-room. He pointed with pride to a special section boldly labelled "Youth". "Take what you want," said he, "and there are more in the boxroom. Here is paper and pencil in case you want to jot down any significant names."

I had not the heart to hurt Joe. Dutifully I made enthusiastic noises and scribbled like mad. It is now not easy to read my own writing and Joe certainly had a bewildering collection of books. Reading from left to right there were: *Youth at the Crossroads*; *Youth and Sex*; *Sex and Youth*; *Youth and the Liturgy*; *Youth through the Ages*; *How to Stay Youthful*; *Youth* (A composium); *Youth and the Pastor*; *Youth and the Psalms* (A Grail Production); *Youth, The Pope's vision of*; *Young Mr Newman*; *Juvenilia* (Verses written on a Playfield Field); *Whither Youth?*, *Why Youth?*, *Wherefore Youth?*, *Which Youth?*, *Statistics on Mental Illhealth among Young People, North Staffordshire*, Part 8.

When Joe and I faced each other in armchairs before the fire, he had to admit with sorrow that his own Youth organization had, temporarily, folded up. "It was flourishing last year," he said, "after Fr Makeshift's visit, but I doubt if it will ever work until I get a proper building, clear of this infernal canal. It is not that they have ever thought of drowning me, it is I who have the ungovernable temper; many a time I have had to beg the housekeeper to lock me up in the garage for fear I would drown some of the little perishers."

Though Joe now had no club, he remained enthusiastic and was bursting with information about Youth work in every other part of the world. He attended conferences annually in Belgium, lectured at conferences in England, had four hundred coloured slides on Christian Youth at Work. When he gave this lecture at Plumhampton, Mrs Begorrah, Miss Anstey, the General, Nellie and Mrs Murphy, who attended it, thought it wonderful. Joe was depressed because the Christian Youth of Mulberry-under-Trill were now no longer interested in work. He produced statistics to show me how the average man, born of Adam, spends a third of his life at work. Lighting his pipe, leaning back and putting his feet up, Joe was eloquent on the apostolate of work.

When it came to suggestions for a practical programme, Joe could only advise me to drop a card to Fr Makeshift, the famous Jesuit, mentioning Joe's name. In Fr Makeshift I would have a man who had really gone into the Youth problem in a scientific way. Fr Makeshift's pamphlet, *Youth at the Helm*, had inspired Joe at the beginning but, later, he found that it had inspired the boys to use the canal.

One tries everything once in desperation, so Fr William Makeshift kindly consented to visit Plumhampton for a Youth week-end. He proved an impressive man, now nearing sixty, suitably dressed as a priest-worker, with pipe, beret and a fawn-coloured mackintosh. He was a lecturer on Youth, for youth, to youth, at the Hutchinson-Ward Emergency Training College for backward teachers, so one would expect him to know a thing or two. He brought with him a bulging briefcase and small parcels of pamphlets for distribution after every Mass.

After supper and over a glass of whiskey, Fr Makeshift told me all about Youth work in Belgium, Holland, France and Germany. From his briefcase he produced articles on all four countries and in all four languages written by himself. Within two minutes, he had me spellbound and signing along the dotted line. For an annual subscription which seemed small at the time and monstrous three mornings later, I was entitled to a monthly newsheet and four annual analytical surveys, Youth in the North, Youth in the South, Youth in the East and Youth goes West.

Fr Makeshift gave me a quick run-through of the spiritual requirements of young people, based on all the latest documents issued from Rome. He advocated for leaders a spot of mental prayer, spiritual direction, spiritual exercises, spiritual reading, in a word, the whole bag of tricks. He asked me if I knew a certain Fr Joseph Plaster, one of the outstanding priests of my diocese. He, Fr Makeshift, had visited this Fr Plaster's Youth Centre last year and, in a limited way, had helped to put it on its feet. Fr Makeshift disliked comparisons but he would go as far as to say that Belgium, France, Holland and Germany would have to look to their laurels now that Fr Joseph Plaster was in the race. I nodded in agreement before burying my face in the current Catholic press.

Fr Makeshift did all that was humanly possible to make his visit a success. He preached at both Masses on the Sunday and invited the Youth of the parish to stay behind to meet him afterwards. Peeping through the sacristy keyhole, I heaved a sigh as my heart slipped from my mouth to my boots. With astonishing eloquence Fr Makeshift was exhorting Nellie, Mrs Gregory, Miss Anstey and the General, all over fifty, plus Mrs Gregory's children and a few stragglers, all under fourteen. Four strange young men in the back row gave signs of undoubted promise but I discovered later that they were Rosarian novices.

Fr Makeshift was not disheartened, for he had witnessed the same small beginnings not only in France,

Holland, Germany and Belgium but, nearer home, at
Mulberry-under-Trill. He squeezed my hand, passed me
just one more important pamphlet, mounted the bus
and took out his breviary.

My desperation looked like blossoming into tomorrow's gastric ulcer, to paraphrase St Gertrude's
lovely words. A few days after Fr Makeshift's visit, I
drove to Little Buckle to talk things over with Fr Vincent
Apse.

"Why come to me?" asked Vin, pretending to look
puzzled. "I heard only yesterday that you were a born
Youth leader yourself."

"Me, a leader!" I exclaimed.

"Yes," said Vin, "I was s-s-speaking to a Fr William
Makeshift, who sang your praises to the skies."

Fr Vincent Apse knew much more about Youth than
he pretended, though, officially, he had no books, no
theories, no leader and no club. He never spoke about
the spiritual life to his young people for, as he once
admitted to me, he was not quite sure if he had a
spiritual life himself. "Father," he enquired, "what is
this s-s-spiritual life that I s-so often hear mentioned?
How can I get one? Do they have a good s-selection at
Burns and Oates?"

This was no affectation on Vin's part, for his mind
was not departmental and he could recognize no clear
distinction between the spiritual and the everyday life.
In the same way, he made no division in his own
schedule between work, recreation, study and prayer.
With such an attitude to life, he found himself genuinely
puzzled when it came to the segregation of Youth. He

only knew and loved people and it never struck him to bother too much about their age, class or sex.

That he was not as simple as he looked became clear, that evening, when I was trying to discover his methods of dealing with Youth. By sheer sleight of mind, he transformed the conversation, spending many happy minutes discussing the merits of the old Charlie Chaplin films. He traced the development of his doctrine through Harold Lloyd, Buster Keaton, Alec Guinness, M. Hulot, Steptoe and Lucy down to Coronation Street. For good measure, he threw in Pope John XXIII. Viewing all these characters, real or imaginary, he proposed his thesis that the noblest instinct in life is the urge to mother other people, and he described the people whom the whole world wants to mother as "the poor loves". If anyone looks pathetic, muddled, slightly ineffectual, like Charlie Chaplin, then everyone takes to him, pities him, mothers him. Vin had got this far when he suddenly started laughing. "Father," he said, "can you s-see anyone trying to mother Joe Plaster with any lasting s-s-success?"

On this particular occasion, Vin left the matter in the air. He finds it hard to draw any clear conclusions but he seemed to sum up his philosophy in this sentence. "It is not enough to act the fool if you want to be mothered; somehow or other—and this is very hard for some people—you must know that you are a fool."

I came much nearer to seeing his theory in practice when Vin invited me to preach in his church. At Plumhampton, we had a special diocesan preacher raising money for the foreign missions, so, for one Sunday, I could get away. When I arrived at Vin's sacristy, I

found organized bedlam, so many were the helpers,
pushing, shoving, taking part in a merry exchange.
Charcoal, candles, cottas, hymn numbers, books, collection plates and other holy objects were raised aloft
by unseen hands. If there was a slight smell of burning,
no one except myself seemed much concerned. In the
middle of the scrummage, Vin was vesting himself. He
was whispering prayers, nodding his head, talking to
the altar boys over his shoulder, inviting a fine young
man of twenty to go to the presbytery and find his other
pair of spectacles. As he had one pair on his nose and
another on the chalice, I could not but wonder how a
third pair would help him in any memorable way.
Every time that Vin muttered "Oh dear, oh dear"—and
these were frequent—three or four earnest helpers
rushed forward to solace him. It seemed to be the main
preoccupation of the whole parish to get the holy man
to the altar in one piece.

When I reached his sacristy, Vin peered at me for
several seconds and then came over to greet me. "My
dear Father," he said, shaking hands, "for s-some extraordinary reason I thought that you were Melchisedech."
My own thoughts at the time ran in a different direction,
I was thinking that if Pope Paul VI suddenly entered
Vin's sacristy, Vin would kiss the Pope's ring and then
ask him to be a dear and put up the hymn numbers; His
Holiness would have gladly done so, for few could resist
the urge to mother Fr Vin.

I became increasingly aware of the feeling of
parochial participation as the Mass moved solemnly
ahead. Even during the sermon, the eyes of the congregation moved from the pulpit to the sanctuary, to

see how Vin was taking it. At the altar, during the cere-
mony, Vin was nursed hand and foot. He produced the
impression that he would be lucky to get to the last
gospel unless everyone rallied round him as they certainly did. When the Master of Ceremonies, itching to
change the place in the missal, asked Vin in a whisper if
he had said the Secret, Vin answered after a pause, "Yes,
I think so, but thank you for asking, George."

When Mass was finished, Vin was still more distracted
and confused. Parishioners were milling around him
while he was praying, laughing, accepting money,
searching for bits of paper on which to write illegible
notes. By the time that he had found his pencil, he had
lost the paper and, when both were produced by some
local guardian angel, Vin had forgotten the note that he
had wanted to make. His was a bewildering perform-
ance. He was not playing the fool, but he knew that he
was one; he was absent-minded because he had forgotten
himself.

And yet, when I invited him to preach at Plumhampton and to help me to get my young people together, he was hesitant, even unwilling to oblige. "No,"
he said, "the only principle that I understand is the
precept of the Gospel, 'I know mine and mine know
me.' Here at Little Buckle, I am a father; at Plumhampton I would be half-way between an uncle and a
hireling and that s-s-simply is not good enough."

It is too early, yet, for me to know if Vin Apse is
right or wrong. I am attracted to his view that a priest
must be a father, not a welfare officer to the youth. Vin
Apse follows an original, possibly unorthodox view. He
does not object to the teenagers meeting in a Catholic

hall if they want to, but he finds it no part of his job
to encourage or entice them, to bribe them with bread
and circuses. Somehow he seems to hold them all
together by the same bond of mutual affection which
makes a good home. Sin apart, and a few dangerous
occasions of sin such as heavy drinking, Vin is interested
in every form of teenage activity. He said to me once,
"Father, I s-s-still cannot s-see why the righteous get
s-so excited; the Gospels s-say nothing one way or the
other about pop music or coffee bars."

After my visit to Little Buckle and its pastor, I let my
Youth Club drag on as before. Cardinal Godfrey looks
down sadly from his picture on the cubs and Mr Mantrip testing knots. The same four older boys drop in on
occasion to comb their hair and talk about the local
girls. But two weeks ago a group of young people
approached me in my study to ask if I would announce
from the pulpit at all the Masses the formation of a
Scooter Club. The rules of the club may be passed over
as less important, but such a mention of the club in the
notices of a Sunday would certainly imply that I
approved.

Frank was doubtful when I asked him, Nellie, non-
committal, the bulk of the parishioners disapproved.
One or two parents feared that the young folk would
be up to mischief, others were sure that they would
kill themselves. Mrs Begorrah, Miss Anstey, Mr Prevêt
and all the Murphys felt that this would give the parish
a bad name. Joe Plaster on the phone was dead against
the project, which would certainly lead to all the
scooterists missing Mass.

Only Vin was truly delighted and urged me to go

ahead. He could find nothing in the Gospels for or
against scooters, nor any known commandment which
would be more likely to be broken on a scooter than at
home on foot. He thought it a very good sign that the
group had approached me as a father and he himself
would take a poor view of a father who stopped the
legitimate enjoyment of his children without a very
serious cause. His only regret lay in the fact that he
could not lend me his scooter so that I could go myself.
"As a matter of fact, old man," said Vin shyly, "I told
them to ask you. They would have gone on their
s-s-scooters anyway, but I persuaded them that they
ought to give you the chance."

There are now ten members of St Gertrude's Scooter
Club and above the printed list of rules is a gleaning
from their patron: "Sisters, if you love God, you will
want to move fast."

Chapter Five

ECUMENICAL DIALOGUE

IF, ecumenically, we may seem to have been dragging our feet a little in Plumhampton, this certainly has not been due to any lack of sympathy. "That they may be one" sums up the yearning of the Gospel story, and Christians of all persuasions must long to respond to this request. It is the practical side of reunion which may seem uncongenial for, whether in private or in public, it is always painful to try to live down a doubtful past. Much will have been achieved when all the conflicting parties accept in practice that errors have been made.

When I was first appointed a parish priest—how many years ago it seems since last November!—my former fellow curates made much of the ecumenical approach. This seemed to provide a wider scope for their particular brand of humour while they had a chance to pull my leg for a couple of weeks. After that, I would be a parish priest, raised aloft at Plumhampton on a pinnacle, well placed to look down on their antics from a great spiritual height.

My former fellow curates took their fun while they could. They pictured me hobnobbing with vicars, putting up prayers with Nonconformists, even offering to play a cornet in the Salvation Army band. "The Family that plays together, stays together" became their slogan, and they went so far as to compose a stanza on reunion to be sung to the low, vibrant throb of four thousand evangelical guitars. I cannot now be certain that I quote it correctly but it was, of course, Fr O'Flaherty at his very worst.

> Here comes the scarlet whore of Rome,
>> Lord, you lookin',
> Sackcloth and ashes on her dome,
>> Gee, what's cookin'?
> Don't say that she at last sees sense,
> Four hundred years of indulg-i-ence,
> Make her cough up her Peter's Pence,
>> That's worth hookin'.

Once free of Frs O'Flaherty and Soap, I could consider the question more soberly and, naturally enough, I hoped at Plumhampton to make a mild ecumenical start. I could find no trace of any previous dialogue in the years before I arrived. My predecessor, after a happy childhood on the Shannon, had Drogheda written in his heart. Nellie, I should guess, stood a little to the right of Cardinal Ottaviani, referring to our separated brethren as "them". Again, though the vicar bought all his papers from Mrs Murphy, she too, like Nellie, was prejudiced. She said "he is quite a nice man, really," as though she was pleasantly surprised that he had not informed against her under the Elizabethan Act of Supremacy. The General had had "enough of those fellows", Mr Prevêt was far more involved in reunion with the Greek Orthodox, Mrs Armstrong-Ffrench came, originally, from that part of Lancashire which knows nothing of the Reformation as yet.

Indeed, only the Plumhampton *Weekly Courier and Echo* seemed anxious to promote any dialogue or ecumenical exchange. Shaun O'Hara, the news editor, whose ancestors had also poached in the Shannon, came to see me personally. He proposed a discussion between the vicar and myself on some burning topic, some deep theological issue like the morality of the Pools. He assured me that he only wanted to help me and the spread of the Gospel and that his paper would be delighted to follow my suggestions, putting a spanner in the works or oiling the wheels. I could agree with the vicar under the telling headline, "Padres in the Pool together", or join issue with him, " 'No Pools in Plumhampton,' says new Parish Priest".

In fact, my ecumenical hand was forced. Joe Plaster, as one might have guessed, decided to give a lead to the whole district with a clerical get-together of which he had high hopes. Without a word to any of us, he sent invitations to the ministers of all denominations and asked all to attend a preliminary meeting in his presbytery. "I did not ask you and Vin," he explained later, "because one must be careful to put over the right image of the renascent Church. I was just a little bit afraid that you might come on your scooter to undo all that Augustine, Columba and Aidan have achieved."

Cocky before, Joe was far less optimistic later, when the first preliminary meeting had been held. "Well," said he, "one may safely assert that it was a beginning but, at the moment, I would not want to go further than that. There we were, all seven of us, very decent fellows, but the whole thing was very, very awkward; I was the only one who took a Martini and I had been hoping to find unity at least on that. I felt that I had let the Church down. There I was, sipping my drink while we talked about Rood Screens; I felt a bit like St Mary Magdalene and that's flat!"

How happy I was that Joe had left me out. Joe said that the meeting had been called to thrash out common problems but that none of the seven had known where to begin. "When we priests meet," said Joe, "we normally follow the same pattern of conversation—a few words about the bishop, the vicar general, bingo, pools, the school debt, the regulars and Ireland, and then we get down to business, who will get St Maria Goretti's, Starcastle, when old Tom goes to his rest? At this ecumenical get-together, I could not tell a suitable joke, even about the seminary. In the end, we all got down to discussing St Paul's journeys, and a very decent

fellow called Appleblossom asked me, point blank, whether Rome accepted Jerome's explanation to Algasia about the meaning of 2 Thessalonians 2.5 ff. It was all a bit tricky because the *Universe* has not touched that particular subject since I was a kid in the Lower Fourth. Anyhow, I said that you were our diocesan expert on St Paul's Letters to the Churches and that I would bring you along next time. I think that you will enjoy the meeting because they have persuaded me to read a paper on Cyprian's use of the emphatic 'And'."

Joe did not read his paper on Cyprian and the emphatic "And" for he lost his voice on the previous morning and the whole meeting had to be postponed. Instead, he was persuaded to join an ecumenical group of blood donors and went off resignedly to give his pint. "D'you know," he remarked on the phone after the transaction, "by this underhand way we might convert the whole of England; funny if some agnostic, with true Roman Catholic blood in him, comes out in purple spots."

While Joe Plaster was giving his blood for the cause, and the Plumhampton *Weekly Courier and Echo* was trying to arrange a dialogue in its pages, the vicar and I made friends in quite a different way. While one cannot expect that the damage of the Reformation will be erased by such a trifling occurrence, yet our personal affection for one another was considerably increased.

The door-bell rang one evening at 9.30 and Nellie it was who answered it. After she had reported that there was a gentleman to see me, she pulled what, for her, was an extraordinary face. Her eyebrows shot upwards with her eyes. I could not interpret accurately her whispered mouthings but I thought that she was saying, "Very posh". In this she was right. Before me, at the door, stood an impressive, middle-aged man, reared, I deduced, on the Revised Version and with a refinement of accent which made the B.B.C. sound second-rate. He was dressed in sober mufti with a tie which might well have been won on the playing fields of Eton, and a suit born in that network of streets just off Savile Row.

Naturally enough, I suspected that he had come to borrow money, for I would have felt equally suspicious had I found a Spanish Cardinal at my door.

He introduced himself as the Vicar of Dovecote, but then, kindly, raised a modest finger to prevent any mis-understanding on my part. "Not Dovecote near Mat-lock," he explained simply, "Dovecote in Breconshire." Matlock or Brecon, I felt very unsure of him.

We spent a few happy moments in the hall discussing the chances of reunion and, of course, of the sterling qualities of the late Pope John XXIII. The Vicar of

Dovecote could allude with easy grace to old Ramsey
and the South Bank clique. He tossed off some mild
convocational joke in which Bath had said to St Asaph
in the hearing of Ely, "A shot of holy water in the arm,
old boy, would work wonders with the Establishment."

He was open with me and, when our ecumenical
laughter was over, he insisted in getting down to the
point. He had to think of his Peggy and he did not want
to keep a weary priest too long on his feet. Would I,
for the sake of Christian fellowship, oblige him by
cashing a cheque?

His was a very plausible story, the old Rover had
died on him just outside Plumhampton and he had left
Peggy—"my wife, old man"—guarding it. He had
flagged a lift to the nearest garage, still open, only to
find that he had no change. He could hardly ask a
garage to take a cheque from a perfect stranger at this
hour of the night. By God's goodness, he had chanced to
see the brass plate on my presbytery door. Thinking at
once of the new ecumenical spirit, he had decided to
risk it and to ask a fellow worker in the vineyard to see
him out of his predicament. "I would do the same for
you, Father, if you ever broke down in Dovecote,
Breconshire."

Now I would certainly have refused—I so nearly did
—had not the image of old Cardinal Bea appeared to
haunt me; there was, too, our own English leader busily
building bridges, and who was the parish priest of Plumhampton to wreck the patient work of years? For one
fleeting moment I thought of putting through a call to
Lambeth to watch the expression on his thirty-nine
article face. I could so easily have insisted on escorting

him to the garage, but just supposing his story was
correct? I could hear his voice, ringing with irony, as
he told the tale of my unfriendliness in some Breconshire deanery. Who knew but that the *Sunday Express*
would get hold of it? In the end I judged that the risk
was not worth it, that I could not plunge England into
the bitter religious strife of the Elizabethan era for the
sake of a dud cheque. He gave me his cheque in return
for £10. He assured me that he and his Peggy would
ask God to bless me and that my example of true
Christian fellowship had put some further meaning into
the great General Council of the Church.

The cheque did not bounce, indeed I was taking it to
the bank the next morning when I met the Vicar of
Plumhampton in the street. We shook hands cordially,
he welcomed me to the town, congratulated me on my
high office, chatted merrily about the ecumenical
dialogue now initiated at Mulberry-under-Trill. The
Vicar of Mulberry had said to him only the other morning, "If we parsons knew half as much theology as that
Roman chap Plaster, we would make more impact on
this vicinity." I could not truthfully praise Joe's theology but I agreed wholeheartedly with the vicar that
"that Roman chap Plaster" was a remarkable man. We
also agreed on the sterling qualities of the late Pope
John XXIII. Our amicable conversation led us all the
way down the High Street, to the great admiration of
the shoppers who saw us walking spiritually hand in
hand.

We must have walked half a mile together before
the thought began to form in my mind. I was going to
the bank and so, apparently, was the vicar, indeed he

said so as we reached the sacred precincts and paused to say good-bye. "I'm just popping into the bank," said he, and then we caught each other's eye.

"O'Callaghan was the name," he said, "and he was a charming fellow with enough of the brogue to make me like him at first sight. Yes, he was dressed just like yourself, entirely in black. He was on a sick call and his car had broken down, so he hitched a lift to the nearest garage, leaving his little dog, Peggy, to mind the wreck. Of course, I had my doubts but he seemed on such easy familiarity with your bishops; he told me such an amusing story of Plymouth saying to Southwark in the hearing of Nottingham, "My Lord, it is in your diocese; you are the one to teach us all the Lambeth Walk."

"Where did he come from?" asked I.

The vicar replied, raising a warning finger, "St Patrick's, Dovecote; not Dovecote near Matlock but Dovecote, Breconshire."

"Vicar," said I, "why ever didn't you phone me?" There was no need to give an answer for we had both been caught by the ecumenical spirit, not near Matlock but from Breconshire.

Chapter Six

LITURGICAL REFORM

PERSONAL relations prove an intractable problem for all human beings and, therefore, for most parish priests. Other parochial tasks may seem more tedious, worrying and wearing, but votive candles do not complain to the vicar general, albs rarely threaten to move to a better parish, the sanctuary lamp does not sulk. On my appointment, I had been warned by Joe Plaster that the church roof would prove my greatest headache—now I have come to prefer a roof that lets in water to a parishioner who wants to let off steam.

A priest, I suppose, is no worse off in this respect than husbands, wives, garage proprietors or undertakers, for even these last-mentioned, sober and responsible people, no doubt have their little differences behind the scenes. Back in the cosy comfort of their funeral parlour, some

poor fellow probably complains bitterly that his talents
have not been appreciated and that he has risen no
further than the foot of the coffin after seven devoted
years.

At Plumhampton, all was, at first, so ominously peaceful that I began to imagine that I had those talents which
make a parish tick. I seemed to enjoy that *Je ne sais quoi*,
an amalgam of theology, holiness, sex-appeal and
blarney which would weld the Murphys and the
Armstrong-Ffrenchs into a sword of the spirit for the
defence of Holy Mother Church. I should have heeded
St Gertrude in one of the most outspoken of her gleanings, "Sisters, trust no man, nor any woman either, least
of all thyself." St Gertrude was, clearly, a woman of
pentrating vision; she penned these words seven hundred years before the reform of the liturgy and the
advent of Fr Clifford Howell.

Normally, social conventions cover up our lesser class
distinctions, keeping us in our own selected circles, dealing mainly and happily with our friends. Thus, after
Sunday Mass, the Armstrong-Ffrenchs make at once for
their Mercedes, *The Tablet* in their hands. The Gregorys
and Ansteys stand in the porch searching for heresy in
the *Catholic Herald*, while the Murphys and Mrs
Begorrah share an Irish paper and weep with delight
that dear old Canon Dan of Plumpatrick had such
successful obsequies. There might be an occasional smile
between groups, a sally or two about the English climate,
but, in the main, charity burgeons inside the recognized
cliques.

The unreformed liturgy always accepted this fact,
may be said to have sprung from class distinctions and

never tried to fuse the *Key of Heaven* with the *Daily Missal* and *Garden of the Soul*. The new reforms, on the other hand, tend to challenge the very foundation of our parish structure with their insistence that, round the altar, we belong to one chosen race. These new reforms are in their infancy at present; soon there will be trouble and many emergency calls for the Vatican Fire Brigade.

Even without the vernacular and a liturgical dialogue, personal relations can be strained. At Plumhampton, there were feuds and factions which a priest may not meet in his first few days. For me, the trouble began when Mrs Armstrong-Ffrench not only invited me to dinner but followed me into the sacristy to do so, a liberty never permitted to the altar boys or sacristans.

Mrs Armstrong-Ffrench trailed me from the altar after
Sunday Mass, swept into the sacristy like a minor canon,
tapped her teeth with a gold pencil and whipped out her
engagement pad. She obviously intended well; even if

she had not, there was precious little that I could do
about it; I could hardly raise my biretta to a perfect
stranger and invite her to withdraw to the body of the
church. The only course open to me, I took, assuming
a wrapt, semi-mystical expression and unvesting with
the earnest concentration of a solitary. Mrs Armstrong-
Ffrench was clearly not contemplative. Utterly indifferent to my liturgical act, she began to rattle off a list
of possible dates for dinner while her husband, standing
sheepishly behind her, took a penny from the second
collection plate and tossed it systematically.

Should I have asked the Armstrong-Ffrenchs to withdraw? With my authorities out of reach, with Manning,
Knox, Heenan and Ripley upstairs by my bed table, I
could but kiss the maniple with added affection and
piously hope for the best.

I gathered from Mrs Armstrong-Ffrench that Tuesday
would not do because an auxiliary bishop was lunching

with her, unless, of course, she rang dear Gerry and asked him to switch his date. No, on second thoughts, she judged it best if I came directly after she got back from the Riviera and before she left for Canada "to look up Mabel and her brood". This, then, was settled and written on her pad. Armstrong-Ffrench, much relieved, tossed his last penny and, as an officer and a gentleman, returned it to the collection plate. "Don't worry, Padre, we'll fix you something," he remarked kindly and, through my amice, I could almost hear soda water fizzing in the glass.

Waiting, dutifully, outside the sacristy door and eaves-dropping from the vicinity of the Lady Altar, the Murphys, Ansteys and Mrs Begorrah were, no doubt, weighing every word. They could hardly have failed to catch Mrs Armstrong-Ffrench's final observation, for she shouted it over her shoulder as she retired through the door. I think she said, "We'll arrange something, Father; d'you know, my brother was a monsignore; he often used to come to lunch with us, just to get right away from it all!" She was actually facing Mrs Begorrah as she emphasized these last words.

Spiritually back on the banks of the Boyne, geo-graphically north of the Lady Altar, Mrs Begorrah checked any hasty words. Hers was an involuntary exclamation which may best be rendered "Hghg-u-hghg". It was her considered opinion that the Armstrong-Ffrenchs had picked up their hyphen and their little "f" grinding the faces of the Catholic Irish —having a brother an English monsignore could hardly erase so black a past. Mrs Begorrah, to her lasting credit, said nothing, but if looks could be translated into action,

I would have been sharing dear Canon Dan of Plumpatrick's successful obsequies.

The point of this rigmarole was only reached when I came to introducing a liturgical dialogue in Plumhampton, a dialogue between a parishioner with a small "f" and a hyphen and another whose favourite word was "Hghg-u-hghg".

It must soon become clear to all of us that the proposed liturgical reforms will prove fundamental, requiring less a change of rite than a change of heart. Their effect could be profound if they succeed in making us all one around a common altar, but you and I may not see this in our day. It will take time to flatten the social barriers which divide us as effectively as the high walls of the old family pew.

Plumhampton is a case in point. While Mrs Begorrah and Mrs Armstrong-Ffrench stared at each other with less love than Carson and Casement, they were, though they never guessed it, members of the same liturgical school. Both were conservative. Their faith was the faith of their parents and grandparents—Mrs Armstrong-Ffrench gazing back wistfully to the day when her grandmamma sipped tea with Fr Bernard Vaughan in Pont Street, London; Mrs Begorrah, to her maternal grandfather who sipped rather more than tea at a Balinderry wake. Mrs Begorrah might say the rosary throughout Mass while her rival picked a delicate path through the Daily Missal, but their common marching song was still "Faith of Our Fathers" and their motto *Semper Eadem*, which may be roughly rendered, "No Change". Both asked no more of the Church than that the priest at the altar should attend to his own business and leave them free to whisper their grandmother's prayers.

When St Gertrude had begged me not to put my trust in women, I had listened; I failed to note her further warning, "Put not thy trust in any man." Women are rarely liturgical and always fighting; I thought—and wrongly—that I could certainly rely on Mr Prevêt. One hardly expects to meet an iconoclast in a blue serge suit. Mr Prevêt had a peaceful smile, a cultured voice, a mouth that drooped to the left when he was speaking Latin, but his knowledge of things liturgical was encyclopaedic and his moral reputation would stand up to any test. Alas, Mr Prevêt's cunning went even further; he was clever enough to praise my liberal outlook and "liberal" is a word that goes at once to the head of a newly-appointed parish priest.

Mr Prevêt attended summer schools galore, liturgical week-ends and other orgies, and he would drop in of an evening to bring me up to date. He could talk for a measured hour on the mosaics of Ravenna or would question Mgr Knox's translation of the aorist in Job 38.28. From Mr Prevêt I heard the views of Dom Basileus, of the Patriarch Sergius of Styx, Wheatabix, O.P., Bomff, S.J., and other experts, of whom Mrs Begorrah knew next to nothing and of whom she would have used that dreadful sounding "hghg-u-hghg".

It was natural for me to invite Mr Prevêt's help in my liturgical plans for Plumhampton, especially as St Gertrude had begged me not to trust myself. Mr Prevêt seemed genuinely humble, denying that he was any kind of expert on Western rites. He had just been lucky

to stay a week with Patriarch Sergius on Mount Athos,
to have lent a hand to Bomff when he was cataloguing
the Coptic archives, to have toured Chaldea with
Wheatabix. I, who had gone no further than the diocesan
pilgrimage to Lourdes, was duly impressed.

We agreed to start very slowly, given the known
conservatism of the Anglo-Saxons, and Mr Prevêt begged
me to leave it all to him. In the spirit of the General
Council, priests must trust the layman and the laymen,
priests. He would, at once, form a small schola to
tackle the responses rhythmically. Possibly they might
begin with the great Amen at the end of the epiclesis—
as he said this, his face became suffused with pleasure
and his eyes showed a strange phosphorescent glow. I
should have smelt a Byzantine rat but I didn't, for Mr
Prevêt held me in a spell. "D'you know," he whispered,
pulling his chair towards me, "when they answered
the great Amen in Gasopolis, the sound could be heard
ten miles across the Bosporus!"

I never guessed, and certainly Mr Prevêt never warned
me, that he held all liturgical changes since the sixth
century as debased. Had he not promised to begin
slowly, and could any liturgical crackpot run amock
with the great Amen? Naturally I disregarded the
rumours passed to me by Nellie, who was certain that,
at Ushaw, they would never hold for a man "like that
Mr Prevêt". I heard stories that the schola was to be
dressed in albs, that St Joseph's statue was threatened,
that Mrs Begorrah had been asked in private to put her
rosary away.

In less than a week, Mr Prevêt had put our clock back
several centuries. By the time that I had worked up

courage enough to put my foot down, St Joseph had been shifted from near the porch to a less prosperous position and an ikon of a certain St Heliodorus of Anchovy hung in his place. Whatever his fame in the

past, this St Heliodorus worked one first-class miracle in Plumhampton; Mrs Begorrah and Mrs Armstrong-Ffrench came to love each other, united in a cordial dislike of him.

When we had our showdown in the sacristy one evening, Mr Prevêt stood silent and in pain. He had the iron control of a monk from Mount Athos but a glint similar to that in the ikon of St Heliodorus showed in his saddened eyes. I had to point out to him, quietly, that Plumhampton was, after all, Plumhampton and that His Lordship the Bishop would not bless me if I transferred my parish to the fifth century and across the Bosporus.

Mr Prevêt's mouth drooped a little to the left as though he would curse me in Greek or Latin but, in fact, he found it hard to speak. He waited awhile, prey to conflicting emotions, and then, of a sudden, drew himself to his full height. "Father," he said, plainly moved, "I never thought that I would ever be forced into a position in which I had to speak to a priest of your diocese in this way. Duty is duty and I must not hide the truth from you any longer; Father, I was deeply mistaken when I once told you that you were liberal-minded; you have been brain-washed; you are simply a slave to the Council of Trent!"

Need I say that I was saddened and shaken? The temptation to abandon reform and to go back to "Daily Daily" (all four verses) was very strong. As always in a crisis, Joe Plaster restored my sanity. "Trent?" he queried, when I had told him the sad story, "Trent: haven't I heard that name before, somewhere? Of course, it is a river in the Nottingham diocese!"

With St Heliodorus gone and with Mrs Begorrah rampant, our liturgical progress entered a slow, more hesitant stage. We carried on with a dialogue Mass at 8 a.m. on Sundays but, though many co-operated in making the responses, the result was no real unity but a simultaneous recitation of monologues.

Mrs Begorrah did her best and certainly made an

answer to the priest's invitation but, whatever he said, she invariably answered, "Pray for us." On the other hand, Mrs Armstrong-Ffrench, though fluent in Latin, was a flier; her aim was never to bring the people together but to get there first. Miss Anstey is also strong in Latin but weak of larynx; God certainly hears her fervent prayers but few others can. The General responded loudly but with a Public School pronunciation which sounded heretical and made many turn round. Mrs Gregory's little girl not only took her mother's mind off the responses but sang an occasional voluntary of her own. Indeed, little Rosemary Anne found the dialogue Mass most attractive as a general invitation for a chat. Nellie regarded it as her task to give a lead at the *Orate, fratres*, after which her mind would wander as she thumbed her way through a large pile of mortuary cards. All that could be said truthfully of our efforts was that some Sundays were very much better than others and that we would never fail completely so long as Frank was there. It may well be that the vernacular, when it comes, will solve many of such problems but, even in English, more is required for a dialogue than an individual, mumbled response.

I knew little more of Frank at the end than at the start of my first year. He was still studying at the Plumhampton Polytechnic though his course was nearly over; he still arrived in good time every Sunday, prepared the charcoal, saw that all the books and collection plates were ready, organized the altar boys. At a dialogue Mass, his responses were competent and loud. Mrs Begorrah and Rosemary Anne together could not put him off his stride. Frank may have lacked poetry or any deep insight into liturgical custom but he approached God reverently and polytechnically. He was neither for the liturgy or against it but, smiling and saying nothing, undertook that which would help me most. Had I handed him a trombone, he would have "had a bash at it" for God's Greater Glory, then cleaned it, polished it and handed it back.

Frank and I rarely spoke save of practical affairs. He could be eloquent when checking over my car, positively garrulous on bus or train connections and a most competent secretary of the St Gertrude's Scooter Club. Beyond such mundane matters, Frank and I never dared to go. He was embarrassed by thanks, seemed to dislike any form of gratitude, never, if he could avoid it, spoke about himself. When he really let himself go, he might get as far as saying, "Well, Father, I'll be popping"; normally he went no further than "I'll be off now".

It was Nellie who put me up to asking him if he had ever thought of being a priest. On such personal matters I was very nearly as shy as he was and, left to myself, I would not have dared to say a word. Nellie, however, is different, always touting for vocations, never afraid to lend a hand to the Holy Ghost. Nellie was sure that Frank desperately wanted to speak about it and Nellie also knew what they would do about it at Ushaw and in the North-East. Naturally enough, I, too, would have been delighted to see Frank a priest. If my first year at Plumhampton, if all our liturgical high jinks led only to one such priestly vocation, here would be reward indeed. All the world over, priests, tall, short, fat, thin, good, bad and indifferent, know no greater joy than when others volunteer to follow in their steps.

I did not handle the situation well. Frank looked embarrassed when I asked him when he finished at the Polytechnic; as he answered, he selected a flower on the linoleum and began to trace its outline with his toe. He said, "Don't know," when I enquired what he proposed to do next. Not thus did Benedict, Dominic or Ignatius win a steady flow of postulants. I was tempted to summon Nellie from the kitchen but knew that no self-respecting parish priest would sink to this. In the end, with my voice jumping half an octave, I put the question, "Have you ever thought of volunteering as priest?"

I took out my handkerchief and sedulously dusted the top of the vesting-press. Frank remained silent for several seconds, concentrating on the flower pattern and his toe. When finally he answered, his voice was also strident; he said almost rudely, "No, I haven't." "Why not?" "Because I'm not good enough, that's why."

One often finds that the kind of shyness which holds one tongue-tied gives way to the other sort which knows no bounds. When Frank said that he was not good enough, one sort of shyness surrendered to the other, and I almost shouted at him, "Good God, don't say that; what about me?" And then I delivered a whirlwind lecture to Frank, still very preoccupied with his toe. My contemporaries would have been more than a little astonished had they heard my description of their feelings of inadequacy. I quoted Joe Plaster's famous prayer, "Lord, I am a swine, as well thou knowest," and was prepared to assert that, though others might put it in a different manner, all priests shared Joe's sentiments.

I raced back through the ages until I arrived at St Peter who, I maintained, felt just as diffident as Frank.

My sermon ended in mid-air, for Frank said nothing and I was left with three prepositions in a row. After a tense pause, Frank remarked, "Well, Father, I'll be popping," and without another word, he popped.

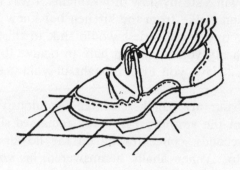

Chapter Seven

ONE YEAR AT PLUMHAMPTON

I. THE PARISH MISSION

I DID not choose the missioner myself. My predecessor had made all the arrangements with the Holy Rosary Fathers, in particular with Fr Odo O'Byrne, the well-known preacher, who came from the same stretch of the Shannon as himself. Whether or not the Shannon would have flown through his mission sermons, we at Plumhampton will now never know. After two cordial letters about his coming visit, came a third to announce that he had been appointed archivist to the Rosarian Generalate in Rome. Such upsets are common when dealing with religious orders but, happily, in this case Fr Odo had been able to procure a substitute. He assured me that Plumhampton was very, very lucky for, in Fr Remigius Killigan, we would have one of the most dynamic missioners of the younger set. I gathered that our missioner was a Bachelor of Agriculture (Dublin), a Bachelor of Science (London) and a Bachelor of Theology (Tübingen). One thing was certain, Plumhampton was to enjoy a rare, intellectual feast. Though I said,

"We'll wait and see, shall we?" and assumed an air of mild indifference, I cashed in and took full credit for the change.

We all worked very hard preparing for the mission, handbills were printed, hymns rehearsed, the pamphlet rack refurbished, the parish census overhauled. Legionaries, Knights, Crusaders—even Handmaids—were out each evening, knocking on Roman Catholic doors. Nellie did out the spare bedroom that the Bachelor of Agriculture, Science and Theology might feel thoroughly at home. I, with my own hand, arranged some of my better books by the missioner's bedside but the great man, when he turned up, had four Agatha Christie's in his bag.

Fr Remigius Killigan proved himself an arresting preacher; he not only filled the church with people every evening, but he also filled every corner of it with his voice. His was a ringing voice and he rang it loud. As far as I could tell, everyone was delighted with his message, turned up evening after evening, went home, evening after evening, happy and replete. Mrs Begorrah was easiest to please, for she asked no more of the missioner than plenty of hell-fire and this she had in large doses, hot and strong. Mrs Armstrong-Ffrench, not so partial to hell, wanted the missioner to come to dinner and her prayer was answered on the Tuesday night. Miss Anstey hoped against hope that the missioner would mention the Family Rosary and this, too, he did with so much vigour that Mr Prevêt was moved to produce a Byzantine pair of beads. The General expected nothing from the mission so he, too, was amply satisfied. Fr Remigius knew all the tricks and when he suddenly whipped his glasses from his nose and pointed them straight at Mrs Begorrah, that devout soul writhed with pleasure and felt that the day of the Lord was, indeed, at hand.

If I was on edge throughout the week, such melancholy sprang from no lack of appreciation; I was sad because Fr Remigius, without any ill-intention, made me feel both inadequate and old. Where only a year before I, as a carefree curate, had criticized my elders with impunity, now I found myself a testy old pastor, a

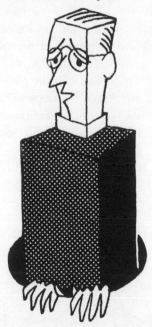

square priest in a round hole. Fr Remigius came from a different world. Younger than myself, he had accepted few of those conventions which my generation had

acquired at the seminary. Thus he saw no need to consult me about my parish, presuming that he had been
summoned to Plumhampton so that, as an expert, he
might put things right. Perhaps he was right in this
assumption, in which case all that I could do was to sigh
in secret and pray for a happy death.

Put on paper my grievances now seem slight. Thus,
Fr Remigius arrived just twenty minutes before the
mission started when I had hoped that he would come
earlier to discuss the parish and its needs. He not only
arrived late but he arrived preoccupied with quite
another problem, how he could get his coat and trousers
pressed. So much did he speak of his trousers in those
last few precious minutes that I began to fear that he
might continue on this theme in the pulpit. No, he knew
his job. Without any trace of preparation, he delivered
himself of a fine forty-minute oration condemning the
new morality. Mrs Begorrah's satisfaction was complete.

When the first mission service was done, we still did not sit down to a quiet discussion about the parish but the missioner, standing before the fire, gave me a short account of his digestive tract. It seemed that he could hardly survive to the end of the mission if, at table, he ate meat, eggs or coarser kinds of fish. Tinned fruit of any kind was off his permitted menu and he shook his head sorrowfully over bread. Luckily, he carried some small Swiss pills in an inner pocket and these, he assured me, would sustain him, provided that we could produce enough cheese.

As these pills took but a second or two to swallow, Fr Remigius had finished his sparse supper while I was still ploughing through his and my own portions of boiled cod. I felt myself earthy and unascetic, a typical backwoods parish priest.

Fish is certainly not the most convenient diet when discussing with a Bachelor of Theology forced to live on pills. Through the fish bones, I tried to plead with him to emphasize, in his mission sermons, the liturgy and the Mystical Body of Christ. My success was incomplete. At every second moment, either the missioner or a fish bone would cut me short. Fr Remigius observed, humorously, that he could see that I was cautious, a theologian of the type which his professor at Tübingen would describe as a "straight-up-and-down theologian" of the strict, old-fashioned sort. He, Fr Remigius, would lend me a brilliant synthesis by an expert—as far as I could catch the name through the fish bones, it sounded like Kold Bath. Anyhow, Fr Remigius, after two more pills, promised to mention both my subjects as this was, after all (ha ha), my responsibility, not his.

He kept his word and, on the fourth evening, he touched on the Mystical Body and the liturgy for three minutes in a fifty-minute address on Pornography. He begged Mrs Begorrah, Miss Anstey, Frank and the General to rise up in their anger, to assert their rights as citizens and to clean up the moral squalor of Charing Cross Road, London. This particular sermon was hardly over before Mrs Begorrah was borrowing paper and pencil to tell Fleet Street what she thought of its moral tone.

My depression, maybe, did not stem directly from the mission but from an unexpected conversation after the missioner had gone. On the Sunday following the mission, Frank approached me shyly to thank me for what I had said to him about volunteering as a priest. He still felt utterly unworthy but, thanks to my enthusiasm, he had decided to take the plunge. He thought that he would offer himself to the Rosarian Fathers, for the missioner had certainly shown to him that this order had an up-to-date message for the modern world. I had never seen Frank so excited or more anxious to express his gratitude.

When I told Vin Apse about Frank, he was truly delighted and congratulated me very warmly on having found another worker in the vineyard of the Lord. Joe Plaster was, on this occasion, more consoling, with reactions nearer to my own. "Father," he said vigorously, "I would have recommended small doses of cyanide in the missioner's supper, only the *Clergy Review* warns us that this rarely works effectively with those under solemn vows!"

2. FAREWELL FROM PLUMHAMPTON

We were planning to celebrate the first anniversary of my arrival at Plumhampton when a chain of surprising changes rocked our little world. Their story may be swiftly told. Saddest, by far, was the sudden death of the convent chaplain, Fr Roache.

A mild, bald-headed old man in failing health, Fr Roache played no part in this story, not because he was not lovable, rather because he never set foot outside the convent grounds. He lived in a small cottage, a little to the right of the main convent buildings, and his ministry was restricted to the nuns. Every Friday I called on him for confession and, often enough, stayed on for a chat. Fr Roache, in his youth, had seen Cardinal Manning; he regarded my other authorities, Mgr Knox included, as young and immature. His one idiosyncrasy was a Latin label, beautifully printed, which he had carried with him throughout his priestly life. Wherever he chanced to be living, he would place over the towel-horse in the bathroom the warning, *"Pater Roache; Manutergium Proprium"*. He said you could never be too careful, especially with visiting priests. I anointed Fr Roache and was with him when he died. He is very greatly missed.

Clearly, the parish could not supply a chaplain to the convent, for many parishioners come to daily Mass. Reverend Mother was on the phone for two full days from Lauds to Vespers and, with the heavenly help of her Mother Foundress, temporarily filled the gap. The nuns had always been kind to others so had many friends. Dear Fr Allsop, the Jesuit, stood in as chaplain for a fortnight; he had completed his doctorate thesis on the reproductive cycle in warm-water fishes and was now busy with research into the death rites of the Caribbean Crab. He had not forgotten his promise to give a mission for me, nor had I forgotten Fr Remigius Killigan.

Dom Heinrich Söndermann also returned to assist the convent. He told me that he badly needed a rest after finishing with Osee and Amos, before turning to the far more difficult Habacuc. Even the Abbot of Pudsey came many times to say Mass at the convent, and one came more and more to suspect the liturgical expression which describes holy women as belonging to the weaker sex.

Whether or not St Gertrude pulled the strings or Mother Foundress or Reverend Mother, a letter from the vicar general next turned up. The vicar general explained that he could not easily provide another chaplain for the convent so he invited me to share with him a wider view. Thanks to urban development at Plumhampton, the undoubted zeal of the parish priest and the existence of a spare presbytery bedroom, he would like to send a curate to help me out. Given a curate, I could take on the convent chaplaincy. The vicar general made it clear that this was merely a suggestion but that he would be up, day and night, in holy expectation until he had heard from me.

My own first reactions to this sensational request were plainly hostile for, after years in a seminary, one tends to look for the snags first. No longer would I be able to read at meals. The new curate might want to go back to the fifth century and align himself with Mr Prevêt.

He might be on a diet like Fr Remigius Killigan. I felt
pleased that I had preserved Fr Roache's Latin label;
now I myself might need to place over the towel-horse
in the bathroom the warning *Manutergium Proprium*.

Nellie, too, was frightened at first and her reaction
pleased me—"Father, it could not be quite the same if
a curate comes." Yet, on second thoughts, Nellie was
moved by memories of Ushaw, while I was converted
for reasons too subtle to explain. I saw with my spiritual
eye a fresh, radiant young curate, full of ardour, and

looking to me for a spiritual lead. Many parishioners
may not guess it but all the old-time aspirations still
flicker fitfully beneath the cassock of even the toughest
old parish priest. Yes, I could almost see myself rising
quietly each morning at 5.30, taking a cold bath, making
my private meditation, and then rousing the earnest
young curate with a pious invocation, perhaps "*Bene-
dicamus Domino*". Plumhampton would then become
a haven for those still struggling to be better, for priests

who could never lose their yearnings for the love of God. So I wrote to the vicar general and though the language of my letter conformed to the tough diocesan traditions, I hoped that he might read of my love of God between the lines.

Four days later came a cryptic postcard which read as follows. "St Gertrude said, 'Sisters, remember that today's thorns will blossom into tomorrow's nosegay.' How right she was. I am to be your nosegay, old man."

I read the signature, "O'Flaherty", with profound misgivings. Though I love him dearly, I could not suppress my first involuntary reaction; shaping my mouth as best I might I said, "Hghg-u-hghg!"